£10.50   TK D

Craft Galleries Guide

A ...tion of applied arts from British...

Published by BCF Books,
Burton Cottage Farm, East Coker, Yeovil, Somerset BA22 9LS
E: cm@craftgalleries.co.uk www.bcfbooks.co.uk
T: 01935 862731

Printed in China through World Print Ltd.

ISBN: 978-0-9550026-49

Craft Galleries Guide

A selection of applied arts from British and European galleries

Acknowledgments

As usual I wish to thank the select team who help to compile this guide:

Paul Bastin for the invaluable help he provides for all computer problems.

Michelle Abadie for setting up the on-line forms and guidelines, to simplify the process of compiling this guide, and up-dating the website.

Paula Downes who continues to keep the office manned in my absence and steadily transfers information to the database to create the basis for the index.

Finally I am delighted that World Print have once again taken on the task of printing and shipping the books, it gives a great feeling of confidence to work with such a reliable team, who always meet their deadlines.

Contents

Logos used on title pages

P Parking nearby Café/refreshments **C** Commissions undertaken

0% Galleries offering interest free credit Principality Collectorplan (Wales)

Regions

1 Cornwall, Devon & The Scilly Isles

2 Dorset, Isle of Wight, Somerset & Wiltshire

3 Berkshire, Kent, London & Surrey

4 Buckinghamshire, Cambridgeshire, Lincolnshire & Norfolk

5 Derbyshire, Gloucestershire, Leicestershire, Oxfordshire, Warwickshire, W. Midlands & Worcestershire

6 Cardiff, Conwy, Herefordshire, Monmouthshire, Pembrokeshire, Shropshire & Torfaen

7 Cheshire, Derbyshire, Lancashire, Liverpool, Manchester & Yorkshire

8 Aberdeenshire, N.Ayrshire, Cumbria, Glasgow, Invernesshire, Northumberland & N.Yorkshire

Our vision for the next two years is to position the UK as the global centre for the making, seeing and collecting of contemporary craft.

Visit our website for opportunities to see and buy contemporary craft across the country, for support for makers working in the sector and information on craft.

Crafts Council
44a Pentonville Road
Islington
London N1 9BY

Phone +44 (0)20 7278 7700
Fax +44 (0)20 7837 6891

Crafts Council
Registered Charity Number 280956

www.craftscouncil.org.uk

Foreword by Mary La Trobe-Bateman

This book is a map to a special kind of world. Recent surveys of the crafts show the wide interest there is in buying hand-made work – it has been estimated that there are over 32,000 professional designer-makers working in the UK who generate a turnover of £880 million each year and that more than 7 million people buy craft objects. As well as this, many fine artists increasingly use the expertise and creativity of contemporary makers in their art works and in 2003 the Turner Prize was won by Grayson Perry for his large pots decorated with figures, patterns and text that illustrate his personal and social concerns.

The crafts offer a great range of work – everyday things that can be used for drinking, eating, cooking; objects that decorate the home or work place; unusual and individual pieces of jewellery and textiles to wear; challenging fine art pieces that stimulate ideas or offer contemplation. Whilst few will suggest buying work because it is an investment, many will say always follow your heart and passion when collecting. Although craftwork can appreciate in monetary value its' real value is that it captures the individual maker's skill, enthusiasm and judgement, their passion for the object, through a combination of the hand, heart and mind.

And from the galleries listed in this guide there is a chance to find the best of emerging talent as well as work by makers who have spent their whole working lives developing ideas and skills. Many of these objects have a depth and intensity not found in commercially produced everyday artefacts; some of them have this quality because they are produced as a result of the maker living and working in one place.

There are many ways of making shown – work that is cast, blown, constructed, hand-built, thrown, glazed, decorated, painted, printed, planed, carved, turned, hand-raised, polished, stitched, sewn, embroidered, knitted, woven – everyday skills appreciated by many of us individually yet no longer regularly taught as an integral part of our culture.

Mary La Trobe-Bateman

Illustration: Textile hanging by Dawn Dupree

British Craft Trade Fair & Design Edge

Great Yorkshire Showground, Harrogate
& Sandown Park, Surrey

T: 01444 246 446
E: info@bctf.co.uk, info@design-edge.uk.com
www.bctf.co.uk / **www.**design-edge.uk.com

The best designer makers from Britain and Ireland showcase breathtaking new collections and design-led creations at these two trade events held each year in April and September respectively. Exhibitors are strictly vetted to ensure the highest standards of contemporary design and craftsmanship as well as representing a broad selection of disciplines. Products on display range from contemporary ceramics, glassware, canvases, sculptures and soft furnishings to breathtaking jewellery, unusual handbags and fashion accessories.

Established for over 25 years, BCTF attracts over 500 exhibitors every year including over 70 newcomers to the industry and around 4,000 buyers. It also has its own awards programme recognising excellence. Design Edge was launched in the south in 2006, replicating BCTF's successful formula and attracting over 200 exhibitors and 1,000 buyers in its first year. Both shows continue to play a major part of the contemporary design calendar. (Also see adverts on pages 335 & 339)

Editor's View

This year BCF Books has gone global. After the success of the mini-pilot section for Australia, in the eighth edition, and the growing interest in International applied arts I decided to publish a book for Australia and New Zealand. 'Galleries of Australia and New Zealand' provides a fascinating read, full of dynamic designs and colourful pieces by makers who are working to a very high standard, some in remote locations. This is an opportunity for their work to be seen by a far wider audience. Please note that as a reader of this guide you may order a copy at a great reduction – see page 333 for details.

With Collect exhibition continuing to draw large numbers, to see the International galleries participating there, I have now introduced a selection from Amsterdam, Delft and Denmark – see following pages. Who knows, this could lead to another book just for Northern European Galleries in the future.

Meanwhile compiling this ninth edition has been the usual roller coaster ride through the traumas of the gallery world. However I am delighted with the final selection of galleries and the improved standard of photographs which the majority have supplied.

I was interested to read an article by Gus Casely-Hayford in Crafts recently, as it reflected my own view, that crafts continue to be considered the poor relation to the fine arts. Although it has been proved that more people wish to buy craft than paintings (Mary la Trobe-

Bateman confirms this fact with figures in her foreword); as Gus suggests the problem maybe the lack of infra-structure to promote and support crafts. We need more high profile magazines, venues and museums. I am therefore particularly pleased to include, amongst our new entries, The Craft Study Centre at Farnham, which provides a valuable service for craft lovers and researchers. Also the brand new gallery for the Society of Designer Craftsmen, who have for years been giving practical encouragement to graduates, as they make the move from university into the real world.

I continue to be grateful for the support and enthusiasm shown by all the participating galleries. Two remain from the first edition, published in 1992: Dansel Gallery in Abbotsbury and Montpellier Contemporary Art in Stratford on Avon. Both continue to thrive in a difficult market due to their enthusiastic and professional attitude to the business of selling applied art.

As usual I would be delighted to hear from any readers, makers or gallery owners with ideas for galleries which should be included in the tenth edition in 2010.

Caroline Mornement

Glass Artists' Gallery

70 Glebe Point Road
Glebe 2037
Sydney NSW Australia
Open: Tuesday to Saturday 10am-6pm, Sunday 1-5pm

P C 🫖 0%
T/F: 612 9552 1552
E: mail@glassartistsgallery.com.au
www.glassartistsgallery.com.au

The Glass Artists' Gallery was established in 1982 by Maureen Cahill, a seminal figure in the Australian Contemporary Glass Movement. The Gallery is Australia's foremost contemporary glass gallery and is the collectors' choice for accessing exceptional works by emerging and established Australian Artists working in glass.

The Gallery has exhibited internationally since 1991 in major expositions such as SOFA in Chicago and New York, 'Tresors' in Singapore, COLLECT at the Victoria & Albert Museum in London, and ART TAIPEI. The success of these exhibitions is measured by the constant demand for Australian glass artists' work for major public and private collections both in Australia and overseas.

From the left:
Jasper Dowding – *Reflective Void*;
Evelyn Dunstan – *Clematis*;
Tevita Havea – *Tamai*;
Joanna Bone – *Harlequin II*

Denmark and the Netherlands

The European Makers Gallery in Amsterdam and Terra Delft in Delft have kindly agreed to take part in this mini-taster along with Cultural Connections CC, a UK based gallery representing Danish makers. They have created an interesting selection to tempt us to make the short trip to their countries.

I hope that seeing them take part will encourage other Northern European galleries to participate in a separate book in the future. I am also delighted to welcome back the Glass Artists' Gallery from Sydney, Australia, their colourful page (opposite) will remind readers why they should be looking out for the first edition of the Galleries of Australia and New Zealand, due to to be published in 2007 by BCF Books. (See page 333)

Cultural Connections CC

P C

Kylling House, 29 Elmtree Green
Great Missenden
Buckinghamshire HP16 9AF
Open: Viewing at above address by appointment only.

T: 0044 (0) 1494 866 803
E: fraserartconsult@talk21.com
www.culturalconnections.co.uk

Cultural Connections CC was founded in 1998 by Birthe Fraser to promote Danish - Nordic applied art in the UK. This was a natural progression from more than decade as Cultural Attaché to Denmark's London Embassy and with a professional background as an archaeologist of the ancient Middle East with particular knowledge of ceramics, faience and glass.

Cultural Connections CC combines an expertise in the Nordic applied art traditions with a knowledge of the actual production techniques ancient as well as modern and can also provide curatorial, adjudicating and advisory services.

Cultural Connections CC has a full yearly exhibition programme. Artists represented in the Cultural Connections CC Gallery:
Inger Rokkjaer, Aase Haugaard,

Hans Vangsø, Bente Hansen, Tove Anderberglis Ehrenreich, Beate Andersen, Jane Reumert, Bodil Manz, Peder Rasmussen, Ivan Weiss and Dorte Visby As well as a selection of Danish 20th century masters

of the ceramic art, notably Gutte Eriksen.

Above: Collect in the Country – Cultural Connections CC Gallery exhibition at Henley on Thames – *leading Danish ceramicists*

Clockwise from top left:
Aase Haugaard – *black pot*; Beate Andersen – *handpainted stoneware*; Bodil Manz – *cylinder vessel, porcelain*; Jane Reumert – *woodfired saltglazed porcelain*; Inger Rokkjaer – *white lidded box with lock ornament, rakufired*; Hans Vangsø – *stoneware bottle*

European Makers Gallery

P ☕ 0%

Spiegelgracht 2a
1017 JR Amsterdam
Open: Thursday-Saturday 12-5pm (and by appointment)

T: 0031(0)2062 23088
E: gallery@europeanmakers.nl
www.europeanmakers.nl

Hanna Järlehed –
sculptural ceramic plate, 32cm

European Makers Gallery is situated close to the Rijksmuseum in the lower level of an historic building on a canal in the Amsterdam 'Spiegelkwartier' area.

We exhibit and sell a wide range of contemporary applied art. The emphasis lies on wonderful ceramics, glass and also paintings by established and new, upcoming artists from all over Europe. It is a challenge to us to bring together, under one roof, interesting and beautiful works by e.g. Spanish, English, German, Dutch and Scandinavian artists and makers.

Quite a few of our makers of ceramics, glass and paintings are often inspired by the landscape, the culture and the music of their native country, and also by the countries they have travelled to or stayed in for longer periods of time.

Each of our artists has had to find an individual solution to obtain the ultimate craftsmanship in his/her own field and to join together form, function and colour.

European Makers Gallery offers you a wonderfully varied choice within the various disciplines.

We would like to invite you to come and visit our gallery for contemporary art and design in Amsterdam. It may well be that on seeing those serene and/or colourful objects in our inspiring surroundings, you will feel that you are on a journey yourself and may want to take a memento of that voyage with you.

On our website you'll find an impression of both the gallery space and the works we show. We hope you will enjoy this virtual visit.

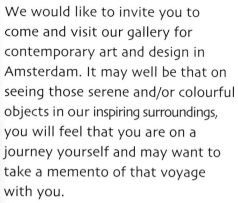

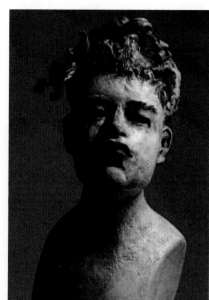

Clockwise from top left:
Paolo Staccioli   – *ceramics*
Ana Rosenzweig – *'Torso' ceramics*
Xavier Hortala   – *'Regarde moi'*
                       oil on canvas
Kathrine Procter – *'Fields'*
                       ceramic vessels

Terra Delft

Nieuwstraat 7 Delft,
The Netherlands
Open: Tuesday-Friday 11am-6pm, Friday 7-9pm
Saturday 11am-5pm

P C ♿

T: 0031(0)1521 47072
E: info@terra-delft.nl
www.terra-delft.nl

Gallery Terra Delft in Delft, the Netherlands - founded in 1986 - is a gallery for contemporary ceramics and is managed by Joke Doedens and Simone Haak. In addition to the exhibitions featuring both Dutch and foreign ceramicists, Terra also serves as a permanent sales point for about 50 artists.

The exhibitions in Terra's own gallery area are regularly expanded with larger shows in the city of Delft. Terra Delft pursues a lively and stimulating policy for artists and the public.

Left: Pauline Wiertz   Right: Hein Serverijns

Clockwise from top left:
Ceramics by Daphné Corregan; Jan Kamphuis; Henk Wolvers; Carolein Smit & Michael Cleff

Dansel Gallery, Abbotsbury – page 62

The South West

6

● BIDEFORD
26

● TIVERTON

EXETER ●
123 ●

46 ●

30 ●

13,104 ●

41

● TRURO 67

84 ● ST. IVES

36

110

73 ● 37 ●

115 ↓ SCILLY ISLES

The Appledore Crafts Company P C

5 Bude Street, Appledore
Bideford, North Devon EX39 1PS
Open: April-October daily 10am-5pm
November-December (Wednesday-Sunday) 10am-4pm
January-March (weekends & holidays only) 10am-4pm

T: 01237 423547
E: mail@appledorecraftscompany.co.uk
www.appledorecraftscompany.co.uk

The Appledore Crafts Company is a co-operative of North Devon designer-makers based in the heart of the lively port of Appledore – a picturesque fishing village with a thriving artistic community. It is owned and run by its members, whose work ranges from fine furniture, baskets, fused glass, studio pottery, original prints and photography to textiles, ceramics, jewellery, metalwork, leather and wood. The gallery also holds special exhibitions – one in early June as part of the annual Appledore Festival, and one in late autumn.

Members value their direct contact with customers and prices reflect the absence of a middleman. Visitors are assured of personal and informed service and an enjoyable experience. There is always something new to discover at the Appledore Crafts Company.

Alex kennedy

Other members whose work is not shown here:
Ellie Bartleman (sculptural ceramics), Beatriz Castro (kiln-formed glass), Lorraine Ditchburn (porcelain), Caroline Lucas (sculptural ceramics/raku), Sue Martin (fused glass), Mary Melling (baskets), Terry Sawle (fine furniture), Bob Seymour (photography and furniture), Bridget and John Stacey (leather) and Judith Westcott (original linocut prints)

Clockwise from top left:
Philip and Frannie Leach – *ceramics;*
Dorothy Sykes – *photography;* Penny Laird – *batik and painted silk*; Wai Yuk Kennedy – *embroidered textile jewellery*;
Tony Worthington – *raku*; Bill and Peach Shaw – *metalwork*

baxters

c ♿

12 Foss Street
Dartmouth, TQ6 9DR
Open: Monday-Saturday 10am-5pm
Sundays (April - December) 11am-4pm

T: 01803 839000
E: info@baxtersgallery.co.uk
www.baxtersgallery.co.uk

Baxters is situated on the corner of Foss St and Flavel St in the beautiful town of Dartmouth in the South Hams. The bright and airy space shows off an excellent selection of contemporary art, printmaking, craft and jewellery. Previously known as Hartworks, the new owner Sarah Duggan took over the gallery in 2006 and has introduced a wider selection of artists plus 3D work in a variety of materials including ceramics, wood, metal, glass and papiér maché. A selection of contemporary jewellery includes a range exclusive to baxters in the west country. The atmosphere is relaxed and friendly allowing you to enjoy the interesting mix of established artists and new talent. Having been a keen personal collector of art and craft, Sarah hopes to pass on her love for pieces that in particular make you smile.

Several themes are evident, a strong inspiration from the Devon and Cornwall coastline captured by many of the artists. Other work reflects a definite sense of humour or the quirkiness of animal-life. A programme of changing exhibitions and the introduction of new work ensures an interesting visit.

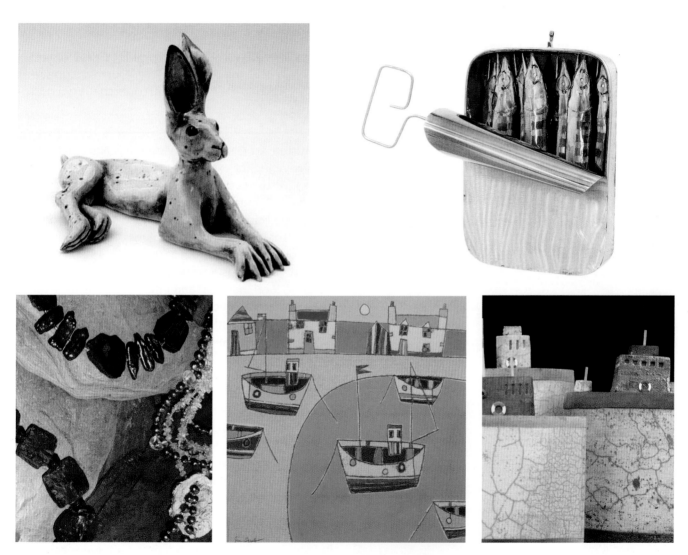

Clockwise from top left:
Sue Masters – *approx ht 30cm x 50cms*; Michael Turner – *stainless steel approx 35 x 25cms*; Richard Goodwin-Jones; Simon Hart – *monotype with gouache;* Annie Stenhouse – *jewellery*

The Burton Art Gallery & Museum

P ☕ 0% ♿

Kingsley Road, Bideford, North Devon EX39 2QQ
Open: April-October Tuesday-Saturday 10am-5pm, Sunday 2-5pm, October-March Tuesday-Saturday 10am-4pm, Sunday 2-4pm

T: 01237 471455
E: burtonartgallery@torridge.gov.uk
www.burtonartgallery.co.uk

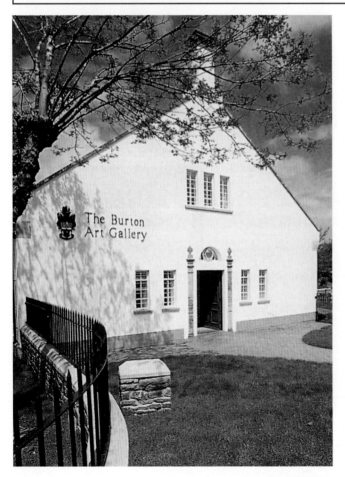

The Burton Art Gallery and Museum is North Devon's premier venue for exhibitions and creative pursuits. Set against the backdrop of Bideford's picturesque Victoria Park the gallery was established in 1951 and completely refurbished and extended in 1994. It now includes three major exhibition areas, craft gallery, café, workshop and gift shop.

The art gallery hosts 20 new exhibitions each year: featuring local, national and international artists, runs art workshops and hosts conferences.

One of the real gems in the Burton's crown is the nationally acclaimed craft gallery. A beautifully lit space showcases work by an impressive list of the region's artists, designers and craftsmen. From jewellery, locally made pottery and textiles, to ceramics, wood carvings and metalwork the craft gallery displays an eclectic and inspired range of work. Artists featured include Hilary Paynter, Blandine Anderson, Svend Bayer, Clive Bowen, and John Butler.

The Burton Gallery also houses the Bideford Museum. The extensive area is home to a rich array of artefacts, documents and treasured items representing the diverse history of the town. Also on site is the Café du Parc. The bistro provides light meals and snacks, and is the ideal meeting place before or after visiting an exhibition, the craft gallery or gift shop.

Clockwise from top left:
Mary George – *etching*; Tim Smith;
Blandine Anderson; John Butler – *wood*;
Svend Bayer; Anne Farag

The Chapel Gallery

P C ☕

Saltram House, Plympton
Plymouth, Devon PL7 1UH
Open: Daily, except Friday, 11am-4pm

T: 01752 347852
E: shirley.margison@nationaltrust.org.uk

The Chapel Gallery is set within the tranquil Grade II listed gardens that make up the 18th century Saltram Estate. The former chapel retains its character with a vaulted ceiling and huge gothic windows, which give natural light and lend a beautiful backdrop to the varied crafts shown. With a long history of the arts, Saltram has an art collection that includes the work of Sir Joshua Reynolds, Thomas Chippendale and Angelica Kauffman.

The Chapel Gallery continues the tradition for supporting contemporary arts and crafts. Throughout the year exhibitions are regularly renewed to fully harness the talent of local artists and craftsmen.

Our aim is to promote a welcoming atmosphere within the gallery, creating a mood conducive to peaceful browsing for our visitors.

The wide variety of work

exhibited in the lower gallery includes original paintings and prints, ceramics and glass, textiles and jewellery. The upper gallery is dedicated to solo exhibitions of both established and newly discovered artists.

Commissions can be arranged. Each year three craft fairs are held at Saltram displaying a huge range of local handmade crafts items.

Clockwise from top left :
Peter Reeves; Michael Peckitt;
Alan Kingwell – *oil painting*; Julie Turner – *glass*

Cornwall Crafts at Trelissick   P C ☕ ♿

Trelissick Gardens
Feock, Truro
Cornwall TR3 6QL
Open: Daily 10.30am-5.30pm. Winter 11am-4pm

T: 01872 861039
E: help@cornwallcrafts.co.uk
www.cornwallcrafts.co.uk

Cornwall Crafts was formed in 1973 to support craftworkers living and working in Cornwall.

The organisation aims to encourage high standards of   workmanship and design and to sell the work of more than 150 selected makers.

In a unique partnership between Cornwall Crafts and The National Trust, Trelissick opened in 1988 amid 400 acres of parkland, gardens and woods at Trelissick Gardens.

This fine gallery is housed on two floors of a beautifully converted 19th century barn. Cornwall Crafts occupies the ground floor, while The National Trust has the upper floor. The gallery plays an important role in promoting both arts and crafts in Cornwall.

The programme includes several exhibitions of members' work with the inclusion of individual focus exhibitions, as well as workshops and demonstrations.

In 2007 Cornwall Crafts launched its new website, which includes a comprehensive members' gallery, and all information relating to the organisation.

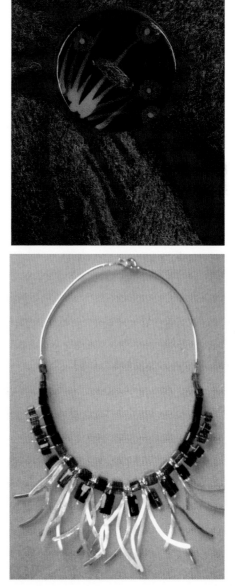

Clockwise from top left:
John & Tricia Christian – *Boquio iron & glass;*
Marie-Louise Denny – *textiles;*
Veronica Polyblank; Julie Murdoch

Cornwall Crafts at Trelowarren

P C ☕ ♿

Trelowarren, Mawgan
Helston, Cornwall TR12 6AF
Open: March-November 10.30am-5pm

T: 01326 221567
E: rod@cornwallcrafts.co.uk
www.cornwallcrafts.co.uk

The Georgian stable block on the historic Trelowarren Estate is the home to Cornwall Crafts' principal craft gallery. Since 1978 the organisation has held regular exhibitions of work by makers living in Cornwall interspersed with exhibitions from outside the county.

Cornwall Crafts' programme also includes workshops, seminars, retreats and social events. A board of qualified selectors sits three times a year to ensure that all work exhibited is of the highest standard.

Future exhibitions will continue to cover a wide area of quality crafts reflecting the standard of work being produced in a part of the country with a strong craft tradition, while at the same time acknowledging the adventurous work being produced by new makers.

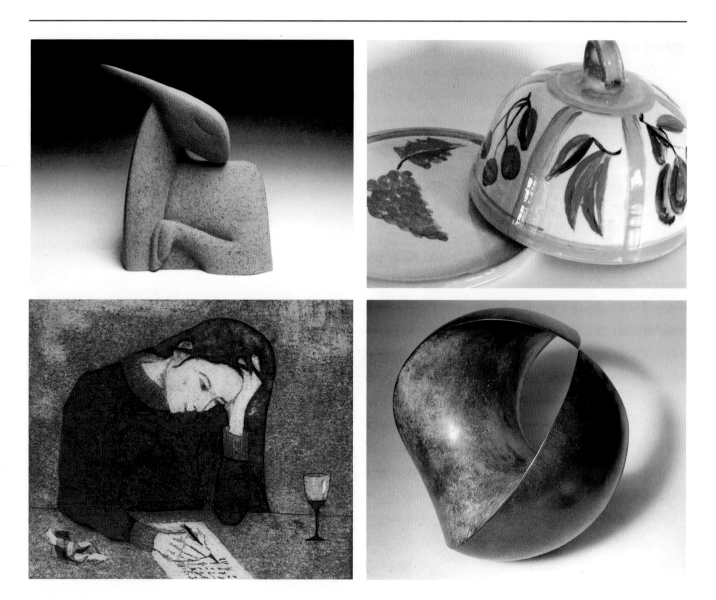

Clockwise from top left: Stephanie Cunningham – *ceramics;* Carol Scott; Samvado – *bronze;*
Michelle Wright – *print maker*

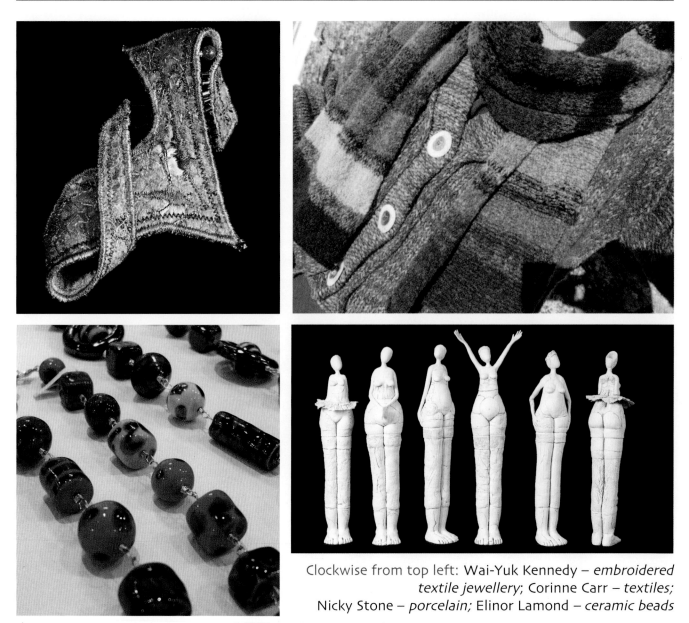

Clockwise from top left: Wai-Yuk Kennedy – *embroidered textile jewellery*; Corinne Carr – *textiles*; Nicky Stone – *porcelain*; Elinor Lamond – *ceramic beads*

Cornwall Crafts at Trelowarren

Colin Moore – Linocut 'No More Fishing' page 115

Cry of the Gulls

PC &♿

2 Webb Street
Fowey, Cornwall PL23 1AP
Open: Monday-Saturday 10am-5pm, Sunday 11am-4pm

T: 01726 833838
E: info@cryofthegulls.co.uk
www.cryofthegulls.co.uk

Cry of the Gulls has a growing reputation for promoting work of the utmost excellence produced by a wide range of highly skilled British artists both from Cornwall and throughout the UK. The gallery showcases the work of many well-established and emerging artists, jewellers, potters and sculptors. The successful website is currently being extensively developed to include an online shop.

The gallery is run by Liz and Julian Davies who are both artists and have over 30 years experience of working in the arts supporting artists and makers through many creative projects and initiatives.

Our second gallery is now open at:
32 Meeting House Lane, Brighton, Sussex.
Please check our website for more details.

34

Cry of the Gulls

Clockwise from top left:
Nicky Stone – *ceramics
Ht 210mm*;
Bev Houlding –
*Oil on carved wood
panel*; Justin Duance;
Cindy Ashbridge;
Dave Pascoe

The Devon Guild of Craftsmen

PC ☕ 0% ♿

Riverside Mill, Bovey Tracey
Devon TQ13 9AF
Open: Daily 10am-5.30pm with some late openings in the summer

T: 01626 832223
E: devonguild@crafts.org.uk
www.crafts.org.uk

The largest contemporary crafts centre in the South West; Jubilee Gallery, Craft Shop and The Terrace – licensed café. The Devon Guild is the focus of crafts activity throughout the region.

Representing over 240 Members (makers) across the full spectrum of crafts from textiles to sculpture and digital photography. Professional development, marketing, selling, commissioning, exhibiting, schools residencies and networking opportunities.

Membership available for Devon, Cornwall, Somerset, Wiltshire, Gloucestershire, Dorset, Bath, Bristol and Swindon based makers. Free Admission.

Clockwise from top left: Ambre France – *jewellery*; Simon Williams – *digital photography;*
Anne Smyth – *stained glass*; Sarah Pank – *basketry*; Simon Ripley – *prints*

Simon Drew Gallery

13 Foss Street, Dartmouth
Devon TQ6 9DR
Open: Monday-Saturday 9am-5pm

T: 01803 832832
E: info@simondrew.co.uk
www.simondrew.co.uk

The Simon Drew Gallery has been exhibiting ceramics since 1981 in Dartmouth. We specialise in British work both utilitarian and sculptural, and stock the work of at least 50 studio potters at any one time.

There are at least two exhibitions a year dedicated to a special topic or one persons work.

We also exhibit drawings, prints and paintings by Simon Drew and John Donaldson.

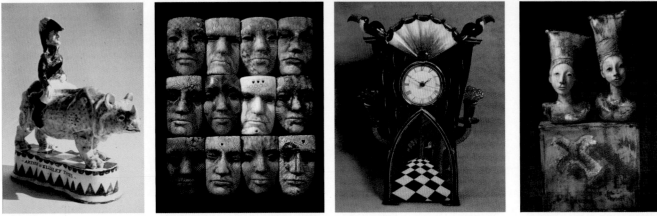

Ceramics from left: David Cleverly – *Wellington on rhino o/a ht 28cms*; Alasdair MacDonell – *Heads ht 20cms*;
Ross Emerson – *ceramic clock ht 42cms* and Sally MacDonell – *Pair glazed stoneware/gold leaf heads ht 26cms*

Simon Drew Gallery

Holly Grace – glass – page 131

The Guild of Ten

19 Old Bridge Street
Truro, Cornwall TR1 2AH
Open: Monday-Saturday 9.30am-1.30pm, 2-5.30pm

c &

T: 01872 274681
E: info@guildof10.co.uk
www.guildof10.co.uk

A co-operative venture by a group of craftsmen/women living in Cornwall, The Guild of Ten opened its present premises in 1979 with the aim of establishing a direct outlet for their work. The enterprise has been a success, gaining recognition from visitors and locals alike for the variety and quality on display.

The current membership comprises Sharon Verry (textile artist), Jenny Yates, Les Freke and Nancy Pickard (jewellers), Mike and Gill Hayduk (puzzle makers), John Theobald (woodturner), Chris Roxborough and Sheila Raynes (dress designers), Oriel Hicks (glass artist), Corinne Carr (knitwear designer), Sarah Bond (childrenswear) and Laetitia Miles (potter).

Clockwise from top left:
Sheila Raynes – *textiles*; Corinne Carr – *knitwear*;
Sharon Verry – *textiles*; Mike & Gill Hayduk – *wood/puzzles*;
Sarah Bond – *textiles/childrenswear*

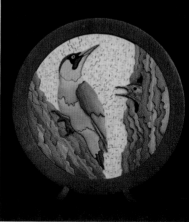

Nancy Pickard

Nancy Pickard is an eclectic artist who grew up on Guernsey. She was showing and selling paintings from an early age, even before attending art college (Central School of Art, London and Cardiff Art College) Nancy's work is characterised by its energy and joyous use of colour and texture.

Nancy studied ceramics and exhibited her hand built pots all over the UK - she had a solo show at Contemporary Ceramics in the early 90's. After having two children and moving to Cornwall in 2002, Nancy took up jewellery making and has become known as one of the regions leading designer/makers in this field. She still makes and exhibits paintings and prints in galleries all over the UK.

Jenny Yates

Jenny works in silver and gold, often mixing the two metals in one piece. Her jewellery can be described as inventive and unconventional. She creates unsymmetrical yet coherent pieces of jewellery that are quirky but at the same time very wearable. Jenny is always developing her ideas and is currently working on a range of jewellery which incorporates a hidden message. She skillfully works the precious metal using a variety of tools and techniques to give her pieces an ancient feel. Phrases, such as, 'love and kisses', 'gorgeous looks like this' and 'ninety five percent angel', are incorporated into the surface texture and done in such a way as not to be immediately noticeable. Jenny has been commissioned to make one-off pieces with special messages for loved ones to celebrate significant occasions in their lives.

The Guild of Ten

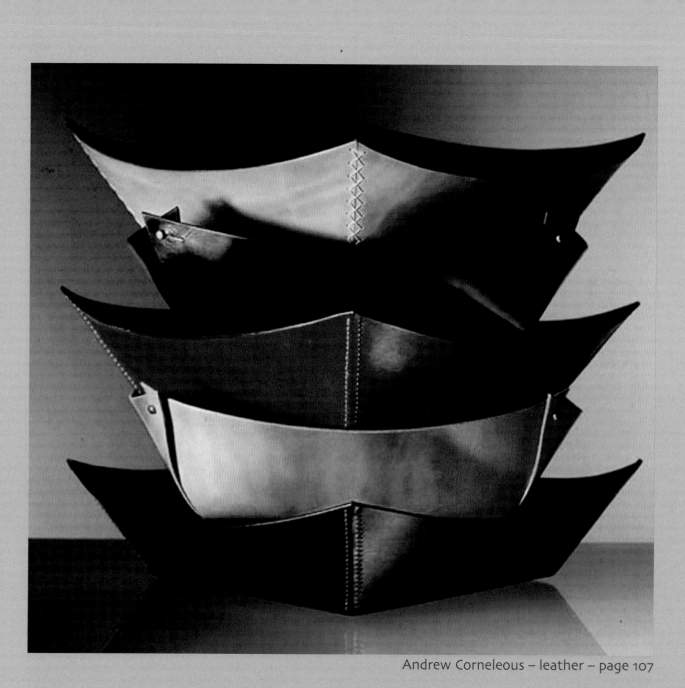

Andrew Corneleous – leather – page 107

Julia Mills Gallery

c

Fore Street, Porthleven
Helston, Cornwall TR13 9HH
Open: Monday-Friday 10am-5pm, Saturday 11pm-5pm

T: 01326 569340
E: julia@juliamills.wanadoo.co.uk
www.juliamillsgallery.co.uk

Photo: Digital Presentations

The Julia Mills Gallery can be found near the Post Office in the popular fishing village of Porthleven near Helston. Its south-facing aspect allows sun to pour in all day – one of the reasons Julia chose the gallery in December 2000.

The building is divided in two, one half being the workshop where Julia produces her glass pieces and the other side is the gallery showing her own work alongside local as well as national makers.

Dividing the two areas is a lime-green and turquoise counter made by Jonty Henshall from materials reclaimed from the old lifeboat house at Sennen. The rest of the gallery interior is fitted in bleached-out wood, which is a perfect setting for the sea-inspired work on show. From Shelagh Spear's magical, glazed sculptures to Sarah Young's linocuts of mermaids and fish, this gallery is awash with colour and light.

Poppy Treffry

Based in Cornwall, Poppy's work is about transferring her drawings into stitch. She sketches whenever she has the chance and subjects can be everything from the roof tops of St. Ives to Andalusian chickens. Through stitch her drawings are transformed, they take on a looser more childlike quality and colours become patterned and textured fabrics. Poppy's work has a strong practical streak; she likes to make things that have a clear use. Her current work includes tea cosies, bags, brooches and framed embroideries.

From the left:
Carole Green – *textiles;*
Sheelagh Sparey – *ceramics;*
Julia Mills – *glass*

Julia Mills Gallery

New Craftsman

24 Fore Street, St Ives
Cornwall TR26 1HE
Open: Monday-Saturday 10am-5pm.
Sundays 10am-5pm mid July-1st week September

T: 01736 795652
E:bennettart4u@hotmail.com
www.newcraftsmanstives.com

The New Craftsman is the oldest established craft shop in St Ives.

It was one of two craft shops in St Ives started by Janet Leach, wife of Bernard Leach and an acclaimed potter in her own right, and in the 1960s Boots Redgrave became her business partner, together with Michael Hunt as manager, a position he still holds.

Both Leach and Redgrave have now died and the shop is owned by Stella and Nick Redgrave, the children of Boots Redgrave, who are delighted to be involved in such a fascinating shop.

The staff are helpful and knowledgeable about the work in the shop and the craftsmen and women who produce it.

The New Craftsman first concentrated on paintings, sculpture and quality studio pottery and gained an international reputation. It then widened its range, and - in addition to paintings and prints by artists living and working in Cornwall, sculpture and a wide range of studio pottery - the gallery now stocks a varied range of contemporary crafts including glass, automata, papiér-mâché, wood, ceramic sculptures, jewellery, and metalwork.

The shop aims to have something of quality to suit everyone and can be found at the foot of the hill that leads from Fore Street to the Barbara Hepworth Museum.

New Craftsman

All photographs by Alan Bennett except bottom RH image by Lawrence Murley

Clockwise from top left:
Sarah Watson – *silver*; Jane Reeves – *fused glass picture*; Lawrence Murley – *stone carving Ht 48cms*; Catie Gough – *ceramics Ht 46cms*; Kate Risdale – *metal sculpture*

Clockwise from top left:
Stephanie Cunningham – *ceramics*; Claire Edkins – *ceramics*;
Lucy Howell – *papier mâché Ht 24cms*; Sans Robinson – *mixed
media miniatures*; Maggie Davies – *hand decorated ceramics*

All photographs by Alan Bennett

Malcolm Sutcliffe Glass Gallery

2 West Street, Penryn
nr Falmouth, TR10 8EW
Open: Wednesday-Friday 11am-5pm, Sat 10am-1pm.
Often open Monday & Tuesday too – please ring to check.

T: 01326 377020
E: info@malcolm-sutcliffe.co.uk
www.malcolm-sutcliffe.co.uk

This bright and sunny gallery can be found at the top of the main street in the centre of the historic old port of Penryn. The gallery opened in August 2002 and is now well established; it was formerly a baker's shop and behind is the bake house where Malcolm makes his distinctive studio glass. There is a wide selection of Malcolm's glass on display and he holds a few Open Studio days when the workshop is open for people to watch the glass making in process. Malcolm also offers glassblowing lessons, please ring or visit the website for more details, you can safely buy online too.

Malcolm Sutcliffe Glass Gallery

Woodbury Studio Gallery

P C 0%

Greenway, Woodbury
Exeter, Devon EX5 1LW
*Open: Monday-Friday 10am-5-30pm, Saturday 10am-1pm,
everyday 10am-6pm during exhibitions*

T: 01395 233475
E: timandrews@eclipse.co.uk
www.woodburystudiogallery.co.uk

A specialist ceramics gallery at the home and studio of Tim Andrews. We carry a range of Tim's own individual raku and smoked work from sculptural forms to more traditional pieces. We aim to promote ceramics at the highest level and also show a changing display of work from some of the leading UK and European makers. The gallery is tucked away with the house and workshop around an attractive courtyard where a selection of excellent quality garden pots is available.

The Gallery stages a major exhibition each autumn featuring the work of some 15 top ceramic artists. Guest exhibitors have included John Ward, Walter Keeler, Robin Welch and Duncan Ross.

If you would like to receive details of this exhibition which runs for three weeks from mid-

September, please write, email or telephone to be included on our mailing list.

The Gallery is situated in the heart of Woodbury Village six miles east of Exeter towards Budleigh Salterton. Coming from Exeter along the B3179 turn left at the crossroads after entering the village and we are 50 yards along on the right next to the Maltsters Arms Pub.

Woodbury Studio Gallery

Tim Andrews

Tim is well known for his raku/smoke-fired work with numerous exhibitions all over the world, two books published and pieces acquired for many museums and other public and private collections. Currently an exhibition is touring in the US and new large scale pieces have recently been purchased by Arizona University, Imerys and The Met Office.

"The challenges of raku, both technical and aesthetic continue to delight and frustrate. Form and surface are abiding concerns and recent forays into larger, sculptural pieces have meant adapting techniques to cope with the demands. Forms often evolve from observations of natural and man made landscape such as the rivulet erosion scars of china clay spoil heaps in Cornwall. I am drawn to the fact that the same natural materials are transformed in an elemental process of creation."

Walter Keeler

Walter Keeler has been working in clay for over 40 years. His work has ranged from stoneware to saltglaze, raku and earthenware. His forms are equally various, with an early interest in sculptural pieces gradually being replaced by strictly functional pots. 'If the pots could not be used I would not bother making them'.

However, his functional pots are rarely straightforward and many have a strong ornamental element with often witty, unexpected details. They bridge the gap between practical domestic pottery and fine-art orientated ceramics - they are beautifully made studio pottery pieces but with highly innovative and contemporary forms.

He is regarded as a foremost exponent of salt-glaze work. His designs draw on 18th century Staffordshire moulded pottery, the forms of Roman blown glass and old-fashioned milk churns and oil cans.

Gallery Tresco

Tresco, Isles of Scilly, Cornwall TR24 0QQ

Open: Monday-Saturday 9.30am-5pm,

Sunday 10.30am-4.30pm

T: 01720 424925
E: gallery@tresco.co.uk
www.gallerytresco.co.uk

Gallery Tresco is situated on the second largest of Scilly's five inhabited islands. The archipelago of tiny islands is located 30 miles South West of Land's End, and it is a 20 minute helicopter ride to one of England's most beautiful and unspoilt treasures.

The Gallery was established in 1992, converted from an old boat shed overlooking New Grimsby Harbour. The Gallery features a wide variety of work by craftspeople and artists based mainly in West Cornwall and on the Islands.

The majority of work is inspired by or evocative of, the stunning scenery of the Islands and their surrounding waters.

Each Autumn the Gallery accommodates a selected group of artists to paint on the island to prepare for exhibitions the following season.

Clockwise from top left: Tone Von Krogh – *ceramics*; Mary Goldberg – *ceramic buttons*;
Emily Nixon – *silver & gold jewellery*; Sue Binns – *ceramics*; Roger Copple – *wooden toys*

Michael Brennand-Wood – textiles – page 101

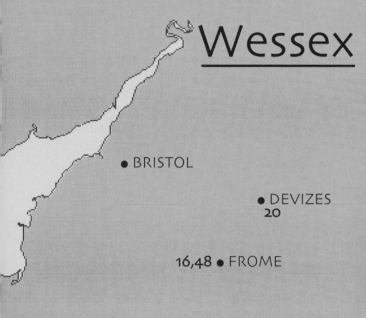

Wessex

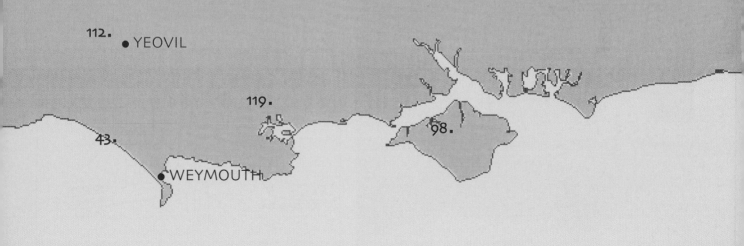

● BRISTOL

● DEVIZES
20

16,48 ● FROME

106.

112.   ● YEOVIL

SALISBURY ●57

119.

43.

●WEYMOUTH

98.

Black Swan Arts

2 Bridge Street
Frome, Somerset BA11 1BB
Open: Monday-Saturday 10am-5pm

P C ☕ 0% ♿
T: 01373 473980
E: office@blackswan.org.uk
www.blackswan.org.uk

Black Swan Arts is a dynamic venue for contemporary arts and crafts, located in the centre of Frome.

Within the listed building are two galleries dedicated to an ambitious programme of changing exhibitions showing high quality innovative work.

The Craft Shop has national recognition and stocks a range of contemporary crafts by well known makers of glass, ceramics, jewellery, textiles, wood and metal.

There are also three studios which offer the opportunity to buy directly from crafts people and to watch them at work.

Black Swan Arts offers educational events including talks, workshops and residencies. The café provides space to relax and enjoy excellent quality food in a courtyard setting.

Clockwise from top left :
Philip Wood*;*
Steve Thompson –
wood;
Gail Kelly – *Linocut on linen;*
Sue Gregor;
Christine Savage

The Bluestone Gallery

P C 0%

8 Old Swan Yard
Devizes, Wiltshire SN10 1AT
Open: Monday-Saturday 10am-5pm

T: 01380 729589
E: guy@bluestonegallery.com
www.bluestonegallery.com

Guy and Janice Perkins opened the Bluestone Gallery in May 2000. Guy has been a full time professional potter since 1977, and for 20 years lived and worked in the middle of Avebury Stone Circle. Janice works as an education consultant, and in recent years has started making jewellery.

The gallery, in a listed building, is situated in a group of attractive independent shops and cafes. The ancient market town of Devizes is situated close to both Stonehenge and Avebury monuments. The town possesses many architectural gems and boasts the longest flight of canal locks in Britain.

The Downs to the west of Devizes are peppered with burial mounds that once held ancient artefacts by unknown prehistoric craftsmen. The tradition of creative British craftsmanship is flourishing to this day, and is given expression in the wide variety of contemporary work to be found in the gallery. We display the work of over 100 potters, jewellers, glass makers, wood turners, print makers and others. You will be made welcome in the peaceful and friendly atmosphere.

Nick Pearce

Nick works with white stoneware. The lining glaze is applied when the pots are at the leather hard stage, and the external glaze, slip or engobe when the clay is bone dry. The pots are fired only once in a gas fired kiln, a two day process from lighting to opening. At about 1250 degrees centigrade a solution of salt and soda is sprayed into the kiln and the interaction of the soda with the clay creates the orange peel effect on the surface of the pots. Nick is inspired by the work contemporaries such as Walter Keeler and Jane Hamlyn, and by Art Deco forms.

Misha Seelhoff

Originally from California, Misha now lives in West Sussex where, from her studio set in a resplendent garden, she creates jewellery and art that is driven by a fierce creativity. Inspired by her garden, the world of art and a love for colour and pattern, the jewellery is created by painting onto a special plastic which is then cut and fused. Semi-precious stones, freshwater pearls, Czech and Japanese glass beads are added to complete wearable art that is individual and collectable.

Clockwise from top left:
S.Young – *glass;* Jan Perkins;
Martina Fabian; Karen Van Hoff

The Bluestone Gallery

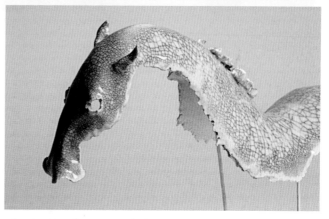

Clockwise from top left:
Lucinda Brown – *ceramics;* David Pegden –
photography; Janine Hadley – *ceramics;*
Laurence McGowan– *ceramics*

The Bluestone Gallery

Dansel Gallery

P C ☕ 0%

Rodden Row, Abbotsbury
Weymouth, Dorset DT3 4JL
Open: Winter 10am-5pm, Spring 10am-5.30pm,
Autumn & Summer holidays 9.30am-6pm and Summer 9.30am-6pm

T: 01305 871515
E: danielle@danselgallery.co.uk
www.danselgallery.co.uk

Visit Dansel Gallery to see cutting edge contemporary woodwork made by over 200 designer craftsmen working in the UK with many from the South West.

Set in a delightful thatched converted stable block near the centre of the village, Dansel houses a superb collection of high quality handmade items with everything on display made in wood and chosen for its design and quality of finish. The range includes individually designed pieces of furniture, elegant jewellery boxes, one-off decorative carving and turned work to practical kitchenware, ideas for office items, toys for children and wooden jewellery. Everything is for sale and highlights the inventiveness and versatility of the woodworker.

Selwyn and Danielle Holmes opened the gallery in 1979. It was initially dedicated to selling their own work but soon welcomed other artists in wood to join them. This has created a fascinating selection of woodwork displaying a huge range of timbers.

A small café serves fresh coffee and teas.

The gallery is near the centre of the village with a private customer car park.

Sarah Nichol

Sussex based woodcarver Sarah Nichol produces handmade sculptures from mostly locally sourced materials. "The inspiration for my art comes from everyday objects which surround us, but which take on a new life and create interest when carved in wood. I chose wood as my medium because of its natural beauty, versatility and varying qualities; I never know when starting to carve what will be revealed during the process. Every finished piece is therefore quite different." Sarah has created a body of work for galleries and exhibitions including items such as rolled umbrellas, baseball-caps, handbags, books and a Bakelite style telephone.

Tim Lawson

Tim started woodturning in response to the effects of the big storm of 1987. Which coincided with his disillusionment with the NHS and early retirement from general practice.

He had always been practical and enjoyed wood carving and other creative activities with wood. He then trained as a woodturner with Chris Stott and was influenced by Mike 'Chai' Scott, Richard Raffen and others.

He has strong links with the National Trust and Royal Horticultural Society, buying trees wasted by storms and disease and selling much of his work through NT shops. He discovered Dansel when visiting Dorset on family holidays and hoped one day that his work would be good enough for this outstanding gallery, where he has sold work since 1998.

Gordon Moore

Gordon's work features simple flowing shapes that enhance the grain structure of the timbers and laminations that he uses. He is a qualified teacher and has taught both woodworking and metal working skills in secondary and further education. He also has a BA(Hons) Degree in Design Technology.

Since 1988 he has been a professional woodturner. He was a founder member of the Devon Woodturners' Association and is the present Chairman of the Mid-Devon Crafts Guild. Gordon's work is sold in various craft galleries.

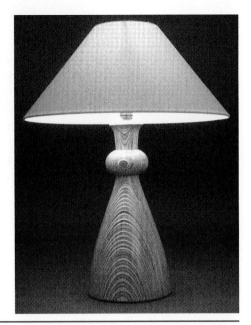

From the left:
Selwyn Holmes;
Jeremy Turner – *carved plaque;*
Jason Breach

Dansel Gallery

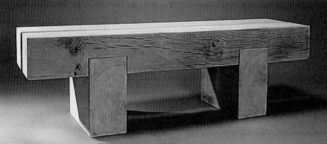

Clockwise from top left:
Judith Nicoll – *also fish bottom right*;
Rodney Page;
Marcus Mindelsohn;
Christine Meyer-Eaglestone – *marquetry*;
Robert Parker

Enigma Contemporary Art

P C ♿

Craft & Pottery Studio

15 Vicarage Street, Frome, Somerset BA11 1PX

Open: Tuesday-Saturday 10am-5pm
please telephone to confirm

T: 01373 452079
E: info@enigma-gallery.com
www.enigma-gallery.com

Enigma Gallery can be found at the top of Vicarage Street just five minutes walk from the railway station or town centre. Showcasing creations by resident ceramicists and founders Jenny Barton and Everton Byfield; the gallery houses such diverse works as richly glazed, thrown earthenware bowls to garden specific, frost-proof figures and vessels.

The Walled Sculpture Garden is a tranquil setting and ideal for showing the garden vessels and sculptures, it is open from May to September.

The Pottery Studio is at the bottom of the garden where Jenny and Everton create their ceramics. This is also where the pottery classes, workshops and pottery parties are held. Enigma is not just a gallery, not just a pottery studio, but a family way of life.

66

Enigma Contemporary Art & Craft

Ceramics by Jenny Barton and
Everton Byfield

Fisherton Mill

Galleries - Café - Studios

c ☕ ♿

108 Fisherton Street
Salisbury, Wiltshire SP2 7QY
Open: Tuesday-Friday 10am-5pm, Saturday 9.30am-5.30pm

T: 01722 415121
E: thegallery@fishertonmill.co.uk
www.fishertonmill.co.uk

Built in 1880 as a grain mill, Fisherton Mill is the South's largest independent gallery. Retaining many of the Mill's original features it makes an unusual setting. Finally emerging from two years' of improvements & alterations, Fisherton Mill is now a vibrant and exciting destination. Spread over two floors the Gallery exhibits work by many leading artists and makers in a rolling exhibition which is constantly changing. The Gallery Shop stocks an array of accessories, ceramics, glasswork, metalwork, sculpture, jewellery and unframed prints and cards. There are also Studio Workshops within The Mill site where you can see stone sculptor Paul Wilson at work alongside other artists and designer-makers.

The Gallery Café offers an atmospheric setting in which to enjoy a great selection of homemade cakes. Lunch is light and modern using fresh produce prepared to order with healthy choices for children. There is a delightful sun-trap courtyard with seating for fine days.

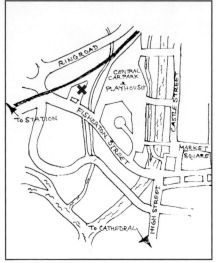

Clockwise from top left:
Paul Wilson – *sculpture, Derbyshire limestone;*
Chris Kampf – *mild steel ht 15cm;*
Zaida – *crewel work;* Glover & Smith – *pewter;*
Pepe Argo – *beaten silver*
& Picasso Jasper necklace

Quay Arts

Sea Street, Newport Harbour
Isle of Wight PO30 5BD
Open: Monday -Saturday 9.30am-5pm

P C ☕ 0% ♿

T: 01983 822490
E: info@quayarts.org
www.quayarts.org

Converted from a 19th Century brewery warehouse, Quay Arts is the Isle of Wight's leading art gallery/venue. Pleasantly located in Newport, the heart of the Island, it overlooks the River Medina. Facilities include three galleries, a studio theatre, a café/bar and a Crafts Council listed gallery shop.

The Craft Shop is seen as the fourth gallery space within Quay Arts, showcasing quality contemporary craft from island and regional makers. Work from over 70 artists is presented including; ceramics, textiles, metalwork, wood and jewellery. The atmosphere is welcoming and friendly and visitors are encouraged to browse and enjoy the extensive range of work that is on offer.

Quay Arts aims to support local artists and provides resources through its workshop complex, Jubilee Stores. This second site comprises seven artist studios as well as state-of-the-art ceramics and printmaking suites.

Clockwise from top left:
Tydd Pottery;
Bruno Charron – *wood*;
Sophie Honeybourne – *jewellery*;
Sue Wilks – *ceramics*;
Neil Tregear – *ceramics*

The Somerset Guild of Craftsmen ♿

Courthouse Gallery
Market Place, West Street, Somerton
Somerset TA12 6JU
Open: All year Monday-Saturday 10am-5pm

T: 01458 274653
E: courthouse@somersetguild.co.uk
www.somersetguild.co.uk

The Somerset Guild was created in 1933 and is one of the oldest such Guilds in the country; in 2008 the Guild will be celebrating 75 years of superb craftsmanship with a series of special events in The Courthouse. Situated in the centre of the picturesque old Wessex capital of Somerton, the Guild has a county wide membership of dedicated and high class craftsmen designers. Members are accepted into the Guild by a selection process that seeks to ensure that the very highest quality of craftsmanship is maintained. The Gallery is open throughout the year enabling our members to show and sell their work to discerning customers looking for something different, locally made and really special. There are 50 or so makers with work in the Courthouse at any one time, along with an annual programme of special exhibitions and events.

Peter Vernon

Peter has developed his own style and is self-taught. He balances an understanding of the properties of wood with his appreciation of flowing lines and form. His work reflects his love of nature – his inspiration.

He works entirely with locally sourced British hardwoods that usually come from ecologically managed woodlands, hedging and casualties of storms. Peter likes to be involved in every process from sourcing the timber to producing the final piece.

Spalted beech and yew are his particular favourites - spalted wood for the unexpectedness of the patterns and yew for its warmth and wonder. His work is continually evolving and shows his eye for form and natural feel for wood.

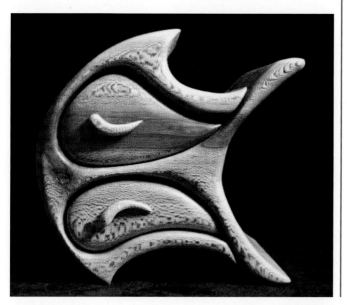

Prue Biddle

Prue Biddle's inspiration for her contemporary precious metal jewellery is always on the move but never strays far from simple uncluttered lines. Her continuing love affair with wave forms finds new expression with her recent fascination with texture, often mixing metals and finishes to achieve widely varied effects. Prue's way of working, making every piece by hand rather than using casting routinely, makes her work highly individual and collectable. She loves to make small series of pieces following a particular design before moving on to something new.

Prue started to make jewellery from found objects whilst travelling and is mainly self-taught. An active member of the Guild Prue lives in a beautiful Somerset village with her husband, watercolour artist Moish Sokal, and their daughter, Rachel, who also makes jewellery.

Frank Martin

After a period as a freelance artist illustrator Frank successfully completed a three year ceramics course in the 1970's. In 1981 he was invited to set up a studio pottery in Bogota, Colombia, South America. He now works on the Somerset Levels, his work which leans towards sculptural is constantly developing and is inspired by many observations and a keen awareness of interactions within the natural world. Frank also undertakes commissions.

Maureen Hall

After a career as a Town Planner and a Town Clerk, not to mention raising a family, I discovered silk painting some 20 years ago.

Having found a medium full of colour and challenge I have sought to develop a wider range of hand-painted silks. I have developed and combined colours and motifs into clothing, scarves and decorative hangings.All silks are hand-painted by me, so whilst patterns and motifs may be similar, no two pieces are identical.

Illustrated:
Satin crépe silk outfit, in black wash blues and greens.

The Somerset Guild of Craftsmen

John Yeo

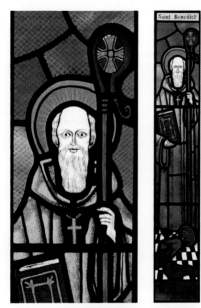

Proud of his Somerset heritage, John was born in Newton St Loe and educated at Kingswood School, Bath. He studied at Bulmershe College, Reading and for the past 12 years has been based in Bowlish, between Wells & Shepton Mallet. He has worked professionally in stained glass since 1992.

Creating principally to commission, John's work encompasses a range of ecclesiastical and domestic styles. From traditionally painted pieces, through Victorian replica windows to contemporary commissions and leaded lights, he provides a full design, construction and installation service. He also undertakes the repair and restoration of damaged glass.

The Millennium Window in Shepton Mallet Church, the East Window of Yeovilton Church, the Nativity and Crucifixion windows in St Mary's, Shirehampton and the chapel windows at R.A.F. Fairford are all examples of his work. He has recently completed a window for Georgetown University, Washington D.C.

Keith Lee

Keith has indulged a passion for photography spanning most of his life. Early years shooting action photographs has endowed him with a keen instinct to catch the moment.

His work has developed into other areas of expertise – especially landscapes, flower and semi-abstract works.

An early exponent of digital techniques, Keith combines the medium with traditional skills to enhance his images to great effect.

Clockwise from top left:
David Appleby – *wood-turning;* Derek Richards – *decoy ducks*; Trish Burridge – *textiles/embroidery;*
Buffy Forgham – *jewellery;* Julie Dare – *glass & jewellery*

Timea Sido – porcelain – pages 251 & 278

303 Gallery

PC ☕ ♿

at Yandles Woodyard, Hurst
Martock, Somerset TA12 6JU

T: 01935 825891
E: 303gallery@yandleandsons.co.uk

Open: Monday-Saturday 10am-5pm, Sunday 11am-4pm
Closed Bank Holidays

The 303 Gallery at Yandles is an exciting new space with a friendly atmosphere and a diverse variety of exhibits from over 100 makers and artists from the South West. The gallery has been developed from the Home Gallery of The Somerset Guild of Craftsmen, to include fine art as well as craft. Renamed and extended, it now offers the largest exhibition space in the area.

Work on show ranges from exquisite miniatures to fine furniture, ceramics of every description; functional for the table and purely decorative. Textiles are represented in silk, dyed, painted and also hand woven scarves, rugs and cushions. Jewellery is especially featured with traditional, contemporary and experimental designs, in silver, gold and even PVA. Various techniques are employed to create sumptuous glasswork, with stained glass panels, lamps, blown vases and bowls and delicate engraved pieces. Based in a working wood mill, the gallery has a fine display of turned and carved woodwork. The 2D exhibition is widely inclusive: with most media, watercolour, oil, acrylic, as well as photography and printmaking represented.

Yandles is an ideal stopping point on a journey to the West Country, just off the A303 in South Somerset. There is plenty to do on site; a famous wood yard and tool shop, hobby and craft department, gift shop, as well as an excellent coffee shop and easy, free parking.

Clockwise from top left: Liz Mangles – *wood carving;* Alison Dymond – *Lariat;* Nicky Clarke – *artist;* Prue Biddle – *jewellery;* Jo Martin – *wire artist*

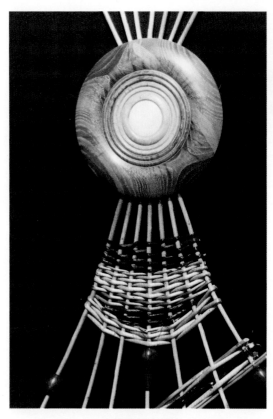

Clockwise from top left:
Jan Sanders – *wood & willow*;
Kaye Parmenter – *watercolour*;
Maureen Hall – *silks*;
Sheila Holness – jewellery;
David Brown – *ceramics*

303 Gallery

Claire Diamond – tufted rug – page 315

Walford Mill Crafts Centre

P C ☕ 0% ♿

Stone Lane, Wimborne
Dorset BH21 1NL
Open: Monday-Saturday 10am-5pm,
Sunday 11am-4pm (Closed Mondays, January-March)

T: 01202 841400
E: info@walfordmillcrafts.co.uk
www.walfordmillcrafts.co.uk

Walford Mill Crafts Centre is the place to visit if you are looking for the very best in contemporary craft and design.

The Mill opened as a craft centre in 1986 and is selected for quality by the Crafts Council. On the northern edge of the market town of Wimborne, the eighteenth century mill is a local landmark set in the idyllic grounds by the ancient Walford Bridge beside the river Allen. It is now a popular attraction, both for local residents and for visitors to Dorset.

This centre of excellence presents high quality craftwork by local and national makers in its craft shop including textiles, wood, jewellery, glass, ceramics and metal work.

There are about eight exhibitions in the gallery throughout the year, featuring work by local, international and national contemporary makers.

The centre is managed by Walford Mill Education Trust, a registered charity. An active programme of challenging courses, workshops and exhibition-linked events are run throughout the year.

Meet the resident designers and makers in silk weaving, jewellery and textiles to appreciate their expertise in creating designs and commissioned pieces.

The Mill has a licensed restaurant The Bistro at the

Mill. Whether you want to relax with a cup of coffee, enjoy a bowl of soup, spoil yourself with a cream tea or you wish to sample a delicious home-made special dish of the day, the Bistro is the place to visit. The Bistro is also open on Thursday, Friday and Saturday nights for evening meals, booking is essential.

There is also an adjacent car park for Walford Mill's visitors. The gallery, craft shop, restaurant and grounds are fully wheelchair accessible with facilities for disabled visitors.

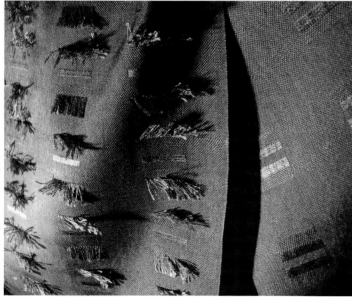

Photo: Caroline Parrott

Debbie Kirby

Debbie has had her workshop at Walford Mill Crafts since 1986. She hand dyes fine silk and designs and weaves it into a wide range of colourful items. Her range includes scarves, bags, purses and cushions, as well as wall hangings and framed pieces, that incorporate hand printed paper.

'My ideas come from different sources, mostly beginning with studies of light in nature and the environment. I am also inspired by architecture and interesting buildings, and sky-lines. My designs are usually simple in structure allowing the silk to speak for itself.'

Anne-Marie Marshall

Anne-Marie has drawn and modelled animals from an early age. She gained a degree in ceramics from Middlesex University in 1992. She went on to set up her studio in the New Forest inspired by the animals around her.

Her travels around the world enabled her to study wild animals first hand particularly in Africa. Anne-Marie's more recent work is based on domestic animals and current pieces feature hares. Anne-Marie uses a variety of techniques to construct her work including slab building, press moulding, pinching and coiling. Interesting surface textures are achieved by experimenting with rolling the clay on a variety of woven and knitted fabric. The pieces are coloured with oxides, under glazes, then glazed and fired up to 1200 degrees centigrade.

Min Fletcher-Jones

Min works in silver with the occasional accent of gold, including patterns and textures to define individual pieces. Her inspiration comes largely from her fascination with unusual semi-precious stone beads and freshwater pearls.

She has been in the jewellery trade since the age of 15. She later spent six years as an apprentice Silversmith, and also studied diamond mounting and fine jewellery at London Guildhall University. Three years ago Min set up on her own and now sells her work in craft galleries, at craft fairs and exhibitions countrywide.

Alongside her range of stock pieces, Min enjoys re-modelling old jewellery and designing one-off commissions.

London, the South East

& On-Line

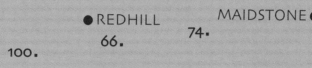

7
READING

●LONDON
4,23,33,34,35,44,45,58,76
89,91,102,105,107,109,117

●FARNHAM 40

●REDHILL
66.

MAIDSTONE●
74.

100.

5 ●GODALMING

British Crafts www.britishcrafts.co.uk

British Crafts,
4 Riverview Grove
London W4 3QJ
Open: 24 hours on-line: www.britishcrafts.co.uk

T: 020 8742 1697
E: info@britishcrafts.co.uk
www.britishcrafts.co.uk

www.britishcrafts.co.uk

From bears in boxes to pears in pairs, British Crafts is an online gallery with an ever changing selection of fine crafts including jewellery, silversmithing, ceramics and much more. As well as the work available to buy, if you would like to commission some work we also have a register of makers. On the exhibition page on our site, you will find details of all the events in the British Crafts calendar.

British Crafts On-Line

Clockwise from top left:
Narissa Mather –
silver & gold;
Heather Swain; Sarah Grove;
Martin Stephenson

Opposite page:
Jennie McCall – *Wire Pears*
Sharon McCormach –
Box Bears

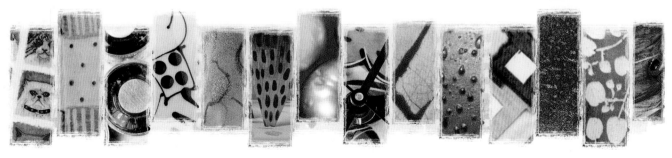

Apple Gallery

P C 0%

3 Wharf Street, Godalming
Surrey GU7 1NN
Open: Monday-Friday, 10am-6pm, Saturday 10pm-5.30pm

T: 01483 424379
E: applegallery@supanet.com
www.applegallery.co.uk

Apple Gallery is situated in a listed building in the heart of Godalming; it is a light, welcoming and open space. The gallery displays and sells art in all forms – from paintings, photographs and sculptures (both indoors and outdoors), to ceramics, glass, wood, furniture and jewellery.

The display, which is updated regularly, has something to suit everyone, whether it's a piece of brightly coloured hand-blown glass, a delicate lusterware ceramic bowl, a sculpture of an animal or an exquisitely crafted piece of jewellery.

On display at any one time will be a large variety of works by around 35 artists, with a regular series of exhibitions helping to ensure that there is always something new to see.

All of our artists have been individually selected from around the country to provide a broad and fascinating range and

variety of high quality works.

Apple Gallery also offers a voucher scheme. This allows several people to either ring in with donations towards a group gift for a special occasion; or to give a voucher to an individual, allowing the recipient to visit

the gallery and select the work they would like themselves.

As a member of the Arts Council Own Art scheme, the Apple Gallery is able to offer customers 0% loans towards the purchase of works of art.

88

Apple Gallery

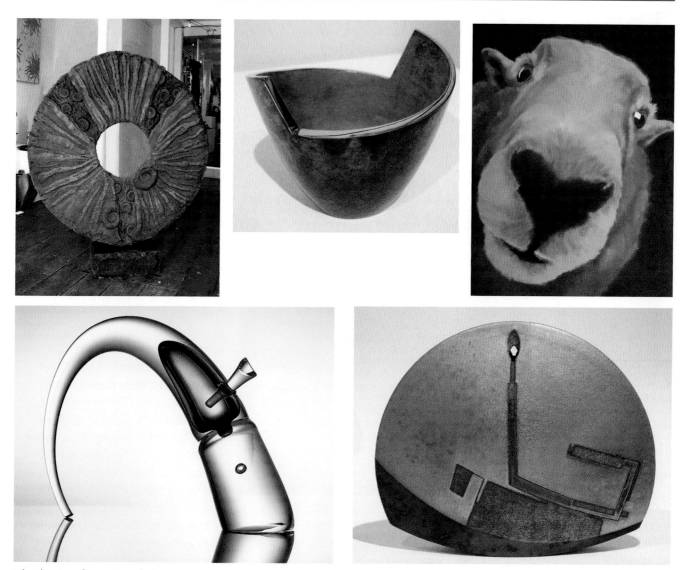

Clockwise from top left:
Eric Duggan — *Bronze resin 1m diam;* Philip Hearsey — *Bronze 6" x 8";* Carol Gillan — *oils on canvas 24" x 30";* Emile Biarne — *Ceramic 8' x 12";* Stuart Akroyd — *Glass 8"*

Apple Gallery

The Blue Duck Gallery

P C 0% ♿

16 Hemdean Road, Caversham
Reading, Berkshire RG4 7SX
Open: Tuesday-Saturday, 10am-5.30pm, Sunday 11pm-4pm

T: 01189 461003
E: info@theblueduckgallery.co.uk
www.theblueduckgallery.co.uk

At The Blue Duck Gallery, calming seascapes hang next to beautiful, big, bright gardens of flowers; while realist still lifes are mixed with abstract landscapes. The gallery also has stunning coloured glass, elegant jewellery, handcrafted furniture, a diverse range of ceramics, textiles, fun and funky metalwork, as well as quirky mixed media sculptures.

The varied gallery content has been carefully selected by owner Clare Varley, and as a result there is a wonderful mix of work by leading artists from around the UK, and also some fantastic work by up and coming local artists and craftspeople.

The many regular events held at the gallery include jewellery evenings spotlighting local designers; solo art exhibitions devoted to UK artists; and very popular RG Art Expo's, which are made up of work from artists based in and around Reading. The gallery has also hosted an extremely successful book launch to which we were delighted to welcome the Mayor of Reading.

The atmosphere in the gallery is bright, airy and friendly and visitors are welcome to have a browse and enjoy the wonderful work we have on offer.

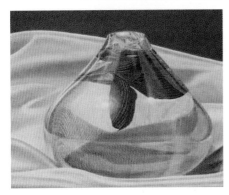

Clockwise from top left: Barbara Shaw – *textile artist;* Kate Williams; Lauren Denney – *ceramics;* Sarah Heppner – *painting/acrylic* & Goodman Morris – *jewellery*

Contemporary Applied Arts

P C 0% ♿

2 Percy Street
London W1T 1DD
Open: Monday-Saturday, 10am-6pm

T: 020 7436 2344
E: info@caa.org.uk
www.caa.org.uk

Contemporary Applied Arts (CAA) is London's flagship venue for the appreciation and purchasing of the best of British craft.

Situated in the West End, CAA profiles the work of 300 members, representing the UK's leading talent. Our members are both established makers and those at the beginning of their careers.

The changing exhibition programme explores the disciplines of glass, ceramics, textiles, wood, metal, jewellery, and silver. Contextual material offers insight into various making processes and creative enterprise.

CAA has a wide range of changing purchasable stock and a full commissioning service.

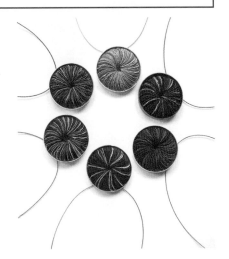

Clockwise from top left:
Natasha Kerr – *textile print (Blackberry Picking)*;
Naoko Yoshizawa – *jewellery*;
Carina Ciscato – *ceramic*;
Bob Crooks – *glass*

92

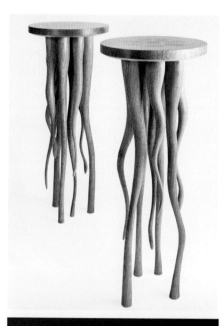

Clockwise from top left:
Gareth Neal – *furniture;*
Sally Fawkes – *glass sculpture;*
Chien-Wei Chang – *metal;*
Lucy Casson – *metal sculpture;*
Claire Curneen – *ceramic*

Contemporary Applied Arts

Contemporary Ceramics

♿

7 Marshall Street
London WIF 7EH
Open: Monday-Saturday 10.30am-6pm
(except Thursday 10.30am-7pm)

T: 020 7437 7605
E: contemporary.ceramics@virgin.net
www.cpaceramics.com

Contemporary Ceramics is the London gallery of the Craft Potters Association. Established in 1960, it shows a continuous display of the work of CPA members. The gallery hosts four major solo exhibitions each year plus one themed show. "Setting Out" which promotes the work of recent ceramics graduates has become an annual feature of the programme. There is also a regular series of showcase exhibitions which highlight the work of a wide range of members For nearly 50 years,Contemporary Ceramics has shown the widest

range of studio ceramics to be found in the UK. It regularly stocks work by some of our most collectable ceramic artists, Walter Keeler, John Maltby, Jane Hamlyn, Phil Rogers, Antonia Salmon and Sandy Brown to name only a few. There is always a comprehensive selection of tableware, and functional pieces including pots for the garden.

The Contemporary Ceramics website at cpaceramics.com provides full details of the exhibition and showcase programme, current work in stock and one of the largest selections of specialist books, magazines and videos. It also offers the opportunity to purchase a very wide range of CPA members work online. Our secure payment system using worldpay and our expertise in packing ceramics allows our customers in the UK and overseas to buy, easily, from one of the most comprehensive collections of contemporary studio ceramics.

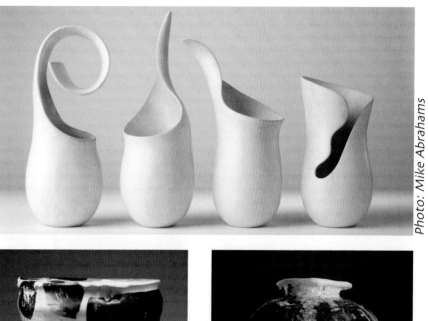

Photo: Mike Abrahams

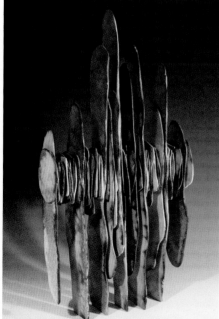

Clockwise from top left:
John Ward; Tina Vlassopulos;
Gareth Mason; Ashley Howard; Antonia Salmon

Contemporary Ceramics

Craft Central

33-35 St John's Square
London EC1M 4DS
Open: Please telephone for details

T: 020 7251 0276
E: info@cga.org.uk
www.cga.org.uk

Craft Central promotes and supports over 400 contemporary craftspeople making it a vital resource for accessing high quality craft.

Two gallery spaces offer a programme of exciting and original solo and group exhibitions. Craft Central also host talks by leading craftspeople and the twice yearly Made in Clerkenwell open studios event. Craft Central promotes the development of new work, innovation and good business practice helping craftspeople to achieve real success.

Crafts range from experimental to traditional; for more information on our craftspeople and initiatives plus times and dates of forthcoming exhibitions and events please visit our website: www.cga.org.uk

Craft Central is the new name for Clerkenwell Green Association.

Photo: Peter Prtichard

96

Craft Central

Clockwise from top left:
Tracey Bush – *paper;*
Emily Jo Gibbs – *silver/fabric;*
Emma Q – *jewellery;*
Katharine Coleman – *glass;*
Helen Beard – *ceramics*

Crafts Study Centre

University College for the Creative Arts
Falkner Road, Farnham, Surrey GU9 7DS
Open: Tuesday-Friday 10am-5pm, Saturday 10am-4pm
Christmas and Easter closures. Admission is free.

T: 01252 891450
E: craftscentre@ucreative.ac.uk.
www.csc.ucreative.ac.uk

The Crafts Study Centre is England's new Museum of Modern Crafts. Opened in 2004, it houses acclaimed collections drawn together since the 1970s by the Trustees of the Crafts Study Centre. The collections include work in ceramics, textiles, wood and calligraphy.

The Centre is at the front of the Farnham campus of the University College for the Creative Arts, housed in a purpose-built new building designed by the A & Q partnership. The ground floor Tanner Gallery (named after Robin and Heather Tanner, great benefactors of the Centre) presents one major show each year drawn from the historic collections. In 2007, an exhibition on Muriel Rose, the founder Trustee and sometime Director of Craft and Industrial Design for the British Council, has been widely acclaimed.

The Contemporary Gallery shows work by contemporary makers. A highlight is the collaboration urban FIELD, which shows new work by Janet Stoyel, Sasha Ward and Yumi Nozake, amongst other leading craft artists, along with shows at Contemporary Applied Arts and The Devon Guild of Craftsmen.

The Crafts Study Centre has received Accreditation status from the Museums Libraries and Archives Council, and is an Arts and Humanities Research Council core funded University museum. Research visits are welcome by appointment.

Crafts Study Centre

Clockwise from top left:
Janet Leach – *ceramic bowl*;
Ruth Facey – *silver rings;* Caroline
Sharp – *willow basket;* Cockerell &
Son – *patterned paper;* Bernard
Leach – *teapot* ; the foyer shop &
a group visit

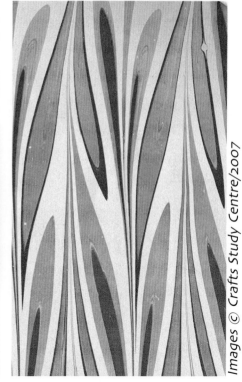

Images © Crafts Study Centre/2007

The Grace Barrand Design Centre

19 High Street
Nutfield
Surrey RH1 4HH
Open: Tuesday-Saturday 10am-5pm

P C ☕

T: 01737 822865   **E:** information@gracebarrand.com
www.gracebarrand.com

The Grace Barrand Design Centre was established in 1996 and has rapidly developed a reputation for showing and selling the very best in contemporary craft and design.

Originally created by mixed media artist Rosemary Hufton and husband David, the Centre is committed to promoting the work of the new and established designers in a relaxed and welcoming atmosphere. The Gallery space hosts up to seven exhibitions a year in a range of media.

The Centre is located in a converted village store and since its foundation has expanded and includes a shop selling Italian furniture, lighting and design-led objects for the home, plus a diverse range of gifts and jewellery. The licensed Glass Café continues to be a popular meeting place offering coffee, cakes and light lunches with wine or beer. It opens onto secluded courtyard gardens and also hosts Café Art where artist's work is exhibited.

The Grace Barrand Design Centre

Rosemary Hufton

Rosemary is a mixed media artist, specialising in work using hand dyed and painted fabrics embellished with stitch. She often incorporates materials such as dyed aluminium, textured rubber fabric, handmade paper and felt, fused glass, beads and sequins – to give texture and intrigue to her designs. She loves to experiment with new techniques and ideas, and also enjoys the challenge of incorporating as many recycled materials as possible into her work, such as wire, electronic components, tablecloths and old ropes to knit various sculptural pieces.

Past commissions have ranged from large wall hangings for an oil company to a triptych for the Millennium Dome made from rubber wet-suit material, hand embroidered and dye-painted.

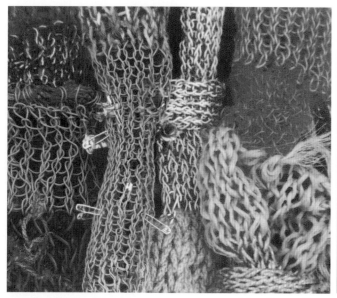

Michael Brennand-Wood

Michael Brennand-Wood, visual artist, curator, lecturer, arts consultant. Since 1979 he has occupied a central position in the research, origination and advocacy of contemporary international art textiles. He has exhibited in major galleries and museums world wide, including the Victoria and Albert Museum, the National Museum of Modern Art, Kyoto and National Gallery of Australia, Canberra. His work can be seen in private, public and corporate collections worldwide. He won The Creative Concept Award in 1987 and The Fine Art Award in 1989 at the International Textile Competition in Kyoto, followed by the first RSA Art for Architecture Award 1990. He was recently appointed as Visiting Professor at Manchester Metropolitan University, and is Research Fellow at the University of Ulster.

John Baldwin

Following a career in publishing and the RAF John Baldwin went to Camberwell Art School to study sculpture. In his 40s he began designing jigsaw puzzles and finding that two dimensional representations didn't satisfy, he started cutting into the surface and so began his involvement in wood sculpture

John's intricate narratives in limewood invariably contain elements of the absurd, echoing the marginalia of medieval illuminators, the anarchy of Punch and Judy and the nursery nonsense of Lear, augmented by a 20th century sensibility. Having achieved a place on the Crafts Council Index of Selected Makers he continues to exhibit throughout Britain and internationally.

Nicola Malkin

"I make large-scale ceramics that reflect my ponderings and obsessions with the everyday objects that I interact with. Blowing-up or playing around with the scale of objects magnifies what is attractive, amusing or just interesting. Most recently this has materialised into giant jewellery, enormous charm bracelets, colossal pearl necklaces and gigantic worry beads; all are used to tell my story."

Clockwise from top left:
Alice Kettle – *textiles*; Bob Crooks – *glass*;
Chris Keenan – *ceramics*; Matthew Chambers – *ceramics*;
Sarah Perry – *ceramics*

Lise Bech

"I get intense pleasure from all stages of my basketmaking: growing and harvesting my own willow, sorting, soaking and weaving with this willing and forgiving natural fibre.

After 20 years of making in a traditional style, I now let my heart and the beauty of the willow guide me. Resulting inorganic, asymmetric sculptural forms reflecting the sensuous, symbiotic co-creative relationship between the maker the material and a life lived close to nature."

Photo: Shannon Toffs

Liam Flynn

"Movement is a major theme in my work. Because I use green wood, (unseasoned) I like to imbue the material with a malleable quality; gently removing the excess from the inside, pushing the wood into fluid forms. The final shape of the vessel is the result of an interplay between the turning discipline and the natural drying process; this is a major element in the design.

My Inner Rimmed series of vessels result in significant modifications to the necks of the pieces. From some angles, the Inner Rim can look like a smaller form nestled within a larger shape. I place the inner rim slightly off-centre with the larger outer opening. I try not to overstate the lack of symmetry, but use the slight difference in height and centre point to energise the entire shape."

The Grace Barrand Design Centre

Clockwise from top left:
Pamela Rawlinson – *silver*; Halima Cassell – *unglazed clay;*
Christine Meyer-Eaglestone – *wood/marquetry;*
Margo Selby – *textiles*

The Grace Barrand Design Centre

Liberty Gallery

P C ☕ 0% ♿

7 Queen Street, Liberty Square
Kings Hill, West Malling ME19 4DA
Open: Monday-Saturday 9am-5.30 pm, Sundays-by appointment

T: 01732 522311
E: info@liberty-gallery.com
www.liberty-gallery.com

Liberty Gallery established in 2006, is a spacious gallery showing a large range of contemporary fine and applied arts. It is located in the architectural award-winning Liberty Square on the prestigious Kings Hill Villages and offers free parking immediately outside.

The purpose-designed light and airy gallery has a large entrance exhibition space with further inner gallery areas. Work from our carefully selected artists includes contemporary frescoes (by Adam Arbeid above, bottom left), collages (by Maria Rivans above, top left) as well as glass, ceramics, jewellery, textiles, leather work, mosaics and sculpture.

Nestling in the picturesque North Downs of Kent, Liberty Gallery is close to the historic town of West Malling (on The Pilgrims Way) with its attractions of St. Mary's Abbey and St. Leonard's Tower and is a short drive from the renowned Aylesford Friary. A very warm welcome and the offer of a complimentary cup of tea/coffee while browsing and listening to world music is offered to all.

Clockwise from top left:

Katy Reader – *Torq Bangle*;
Emily Morgan – *Melt Me*;
Annie Ross – *glass*;
Andrew Corneleous – *leather*;
William Jordan –
wire sculpture Ht 150cms x 110cms long;
Claire Palastanga – *ceramics*

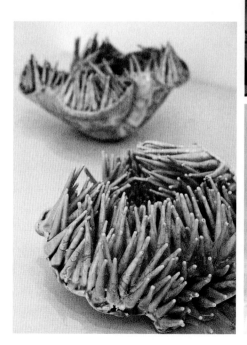

Oxo Tower Wharf

Oxo Tower Wharf
Bargehouse Street
South Bank SE1 9PH

E: oxo@coin-street.org
www.oxotower.co.uk

All photos on page 116/7 by Alan Vallis

You may have walked along London's Southbank, and passed the landmark Oxo Tower once the home of the OXO cube, which was made and exported from here, all over the world.

It is now a thriving mixed use development including galleries community housing, shops and design studios.

The following pages present a taste of the selection to be found at the Oxo Tower Wharf and nearby Gabriel's Wharf.

All those featured are small businesses run by designer makers. There is also a range of bars, cafés and restaurants with indoor and outdoor seating, where you may relax after exploring these Aladdin's Caves.

Oxo Tower Wharf & Gabriel's Wharf

Gabriel's Wharf

Gabriel's Wharf
56 Upper Ground
London SE1 9PP

E: oxo@coin-street.org
www.gabrielswharf.co.uk

GABRIEL'S WHARF GALLERIES

David Ashton Jewellery

Davies & Vaughan

Southbank Printmakers

Gabriel's Wharf started life over 18 years ago, as a tenuous community of designer makers, amidst the major changes which were happening along the Southbank. It has now grown into a flourishing group of established designer workshops, restaurants and bars and hosts a number of summer festivals and music events.

The first three galleries featured in this section are from Gabriel's Wharf, the remainder from Oxo Tower Wharf – please check the logos in the title bars. The location map shows both venues.

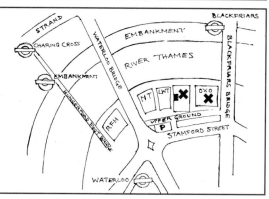

Oxo Tower Wharf & Gabriel's Wharf

David Ashton Jewellery

P C

Shop 6, Gabriel's Wharf
56 Upper Ground, London SE1 9PP
Open: Tuesday-Friday 11am-5.30pm, Saturdays 11am-5pm

T: 020 7401 2405
E: info@davidashton.co.uk
www.davidashton.co.uk

David Ashton jewellery has been trading for over 23 years, and currently has a joint shop/workshop in Gabriel's Wharf on the South Bank in London.

Offering a mainly bespoke service, designs are original and instantly recognisable. It is important not to limit the customers' choices, so it is very important that the shop and workshop are combined so that the customer can interact with the person who will be manufacturing their purchase. I like to think that each piece is individually designed for the wearer. I run adverts in many national magazines and newspapers, which is how customers first get to know my designs. Many customers return for more purchases and recommend me to friends and family.

It is possible to mail-order via the brochure although most customers will come into the shop and discuss their particular needs. I also sell products from stock I've made and bought in.

Right from the top:
* Platinum and diamond ring
*Three interlocking platinum bands
with sapphires & diamonds
*Pair 18ct yellow and white gold rings, with
Marquise cut natural rubies and diamonds

Rings can be made in any of the three 18ct gold colours, yellow, rose and white or platinum with a variety of band widths available and settings in any colour. However, please note that not all the patterned bands are available in all the colours.

The quantity, size and position of small diamonds set flush into a band may be varied. A choice of centre stone is also available in addition to size, cut and colour, although we consider diamond (colourless and coloured), ruby or Sapphire to be the most suitable for daily wear. The equivalent size Sapphire or ruby in place of diamond will result in a significant reduction in cost.

Commissions take six weeks to complete and a deposit of 25% is required before commencing work. (If such time is unavailable, please phone before ordering).

———— 18 ct gold and platinum rings ————
with various precious stones

Davies & Vaughan

GABRIEL'S WHARF

15 Gabriel's Wharf, London SE1 9PP
Open: Monday-Friday 11am-5.30pm, Saturday 11am-5pm. Please call to check if making a special trip.

T: 020 7928 8808
E: kutu@globalnet.co.uk
www.daviesandvaughan.co.u

The small shop and workshop at Gabriel's Wharf is run by Bo Davies and Malcolm Vaughan who have been making jewellery since 1980.

The shop is really a glorified workshop with display windows showing a range of individual silver, gold and platinum items. We also specialise in making personal items; engagement and wedding bands; anniversary and birthday gifts or tokens for loved ones.

Having a workshop means that we can cater for the client's desires on the spot. From initial concept to the finished pieces. Each part of the design is given careful consideration. The choice of metal; the colours and the selection of the appropriate gems. Each part of the process is undertaken with diligence; very small changes can make all the difference to the finished design.

Clockwise from top left:
*Ring – fine amethyst set in 18ct yellow gold and diamonds.
*Ring – fine emerald set in platinum with pave set diamonds.
*Ring – sapphire with triangular diamonds, set in 18ct yellow gold on platinum shank *Brooch – silver with gold sun

Clockwise from top left:
*Necklace, silver 18ct golds, sapphires; *Brooch, silver & onyx;
*Brooch, 18ct white gold and rubies; *detail of silver brooch with 18ct
yellow gold fish & *belt buckle, oxidised silver.

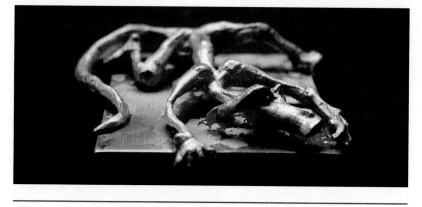

Our work is worn by Lords and Ladies, the stars of
stage and screen and now by the children of many
of our first clients who have grown up to buy their
own jewels.

Davies & Vaughan

Southbank Printmakers

GABRIEL'S WHARF

Unit 12 Gabriel's Wharf
56 Upper Ground, London SE1
Open: Daily from 11.30am except 25th, 26th Dec and 1st Jan

T: 020 7928 8184
www.southbankprintmakers.com

Above: Susie Perring – *aquatint*
Below: Theresa Pateman –
etching with aquatint

Left: Pip
Carpenter –
collagraph;
Right:
Mary Cossey
– *aquatint*

Clockwise from top left:
Diana Croft – *collagraph;*
Mychael Barratt – *etching;*
Emiko Aida – *aquatint;*
Colin Moore – *linocut;*
Susie Perring – *aquatint;*

Oxo Tower Wharf

Oxo Tower Wharf
Bargehouse Street
South Bank SE1 9PH

E: oxo@coin-street.org
www.oxotower.co.uk

OXO TOWER WHARF GALLERIES

Anne Kyyrö Quinn

little + collins

onebravo

Skylark 2 Gallery

Studio Fusion

Alan Vallis @ OXO

Anne Kyyrö Quinn

2.06 Oxo Tower Wharf, Bargehouse Street
London SE1 9PH
Open: Monday-Friday 10am-6 pm, weekend by appointment

c

T: 020 7021 0702
E: info@annekyyroquinn.com
www.annekyyroquinn.com

With their sleek silhouettes, minimal motifs and textural surfaces, the fabrics designed by Anne Kyyrö Quinn are some of the most visionary expressions of interior textiles today.

One of the first designers to rediscover felt and update it for the contemporary market, Kyyrö Quinn broke fresh ground when she used this material to pioneer a new range of unusually structured textiles.

Based on the second floor of the Oxo Tower Kyyrö Quinn boasts an impressive product range including cushions, lighting and table accessories.

The most striking of all are the wall panels which aim to bridge the gap between urban interiors and natural landscape. The inherent sound absorbency of felt gives these panels the ideal properties for transforming large open plan areas into an oasis of calm. The 3D textural wallcoverings not only diffuse

the sound but add a sumptuous backdrop and individual feel.

As Kyyrö Quinn explains, "Stretching textiles across a large surface area not only softens an interior yet creates an incredibly rich backdrop". Please check the website for the full range or contact the studio to discuss requests further.

Clockwise from top left:
Block cushions;
Red Leaf wall panel installation;
White Rosette wall panel installation; Orange Tulip detail.

little+collins

2.10 Oxo Tower Wharf (Second Floor Courtyard)
Bargehouse Street
South Bank, London SE1 9PH
*Open: Monday-Friday 11am-6pm other times
and commissions by appointment*

T: 020 7928 9022
E: jenni.teresa@littlecollins.co.uk
www.littlecollins.co.uk

Established over 15 years ago, Little + Collins design and make contemporary collections of hand tufted rugs, runners and wall hangings. A selection of these can be seen at their studio gallery at the Oxo Tower. Creativity, craftsmanship and quality are hallmarks of Little + Collins' work, which uses best quality New Zealand wool.

Jenni Little and Teresa Collins are textile designers, renowned for their use of delicious subtle colour and refined texture. The limited edition collections have a distinct design identity and sensual colour palette inspired by landscape and architecture, creating an appeal that is as tactile as it is visual.

We frequently work closely with individuals on bespoke commissions to create a highly collectable piece of textile art.

onebravo

2.01Oxo Tower Wharf (Second Floor Courtyard)
Bargehouse Street, South Bank
London SE1 9PH
Open: Monday-Friday 9am-6pm, Saturday 12-4pm

T: 020 7921 9298
E: info@onebravo.com
www.onebravo.com

onebravo is an international design and craft partnership which focuses on interior products, principally mirrors and mosaic, all handmade from the finest materials. Their focus is innovation through an ever-changing range. onebravo strive for personality and individuality, while maintaining quality and consistency.

They design and create for people and spaces as well as for values and tastes. These drive their business and shape their designs.

All designs:
Arturo Gonzalez
Bravo – *wood &
stained glass*

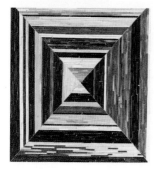

Skylark 2 Gallery

1.09 Oxo Tower Wharf (First Floor Riverside)
Bargehouse Street, London SE1 9PH
Open: Tuesday-Sunday 11am-6pm

P C ☕ 0% ♿

T: 020 7401 9666
E: info@skylarkgallery.com
www.skylarkgallery.com

Skylark 2 Gallery is run by its artist members. It opened in 2001 on the first floor walkway of the Oxo Tower building, overlooking the Thames. It is filled with varied and vibrant, affordable works from 17 contemporary member artists; a sumptuous selection of sculpture, ceramics, paintings and prints can be seen.

The gallery is always warm and welcoming, the displays are constantly changing and visitors can meet and talk directly with the artists/makers on duty. The sister gallery; Skylark 1 is nearby in Gabriel's Wharf.

From the left: Ruty Benjamini; Ludwig Wagner; Ruth Allen; Jasmine Pradissitto; Gill Hickman & Trinidad Ball

Vicky Oldfield

Vicky's artwork incorporates drawing and print. Bold mark making, texture and process bring the pictures to life.

She produces small print editions, often mixing media and finishing works off by hand, making each a one-off. Vicky's aim is to create atmospheric images that capture the essence of form and the feeling of a time and a place.

Left – Agapanthus
Right – Shaving Brush
www.vickyoldfield.co.uk

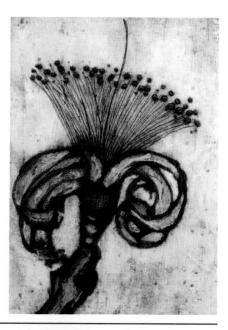

Ruty Benjamini

Ruty was born in Israel. She studied ceramics at Camberwell School of Art. She travelled in Europe and India and lived in Southern Italy. Ruty now lives and works in South London and teaches pottery to adults and the elderly.

Ruty's work is inspired by natural forms, the human body, weathered and effaced surfaces, ancient pottery, and the fusion of human traces with nature.

She sees her work as a personal journey exploring identity, connecting to roots, and expressing the process of growth, evolution and the layering that make up a whole.

Ruty makes one-off and family groups of organic, sculptural vessels, plates and figurines. She often starts by throwing on the wheel. The thrown components are stretched, torn and reconstructed intuitively, with attention to drawn lines and clay effects.

Studio Fusion Gallery

1.06 Oxo Tower Wharf
(First Floor Riverside)
Bargehouse Street, London SE1 9PH
Open: Tuesday-Sunday 11am-6pm

T: 020 7928 3600
E: info@studiofusiongallery.co.uk
www.studiofusiongallery.co.uk

Studio Fusion is the first applied art gallery in the UK specialising in a contemporary approach to enamel. In addition to jewellery and silverware in precious metals, there are also larger two and three dimensional items in copper and steel.

Opened in 1996 by a co-operative of six women artists, the gallery showcases their work, as well as organising an annual programme of special exhibitions by leading British and international artists, whose work is varied, innovative and highly individual.

Sarah Letts makes delicately engraved and enamelled jewellery, each with its own distinct identity and signature embodying memories, while **Joan MacKarell's** bold bead

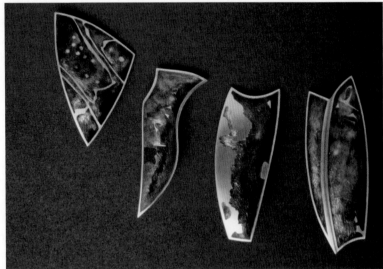

Above: Sarah Letts – *silver & enamel brooches*

necklaces, subtly enamelled, are also inspired by fragments of memory and the patina of time. **Louise O'Neill's** 18ct gold sculptural jewellery includes engagement and wedding ring commissions and intriguing, subtly coloured precious and semiprecious stone stacking ring sets. **Gudde Jane Skyrme** combines jewellery and printmaking with subtly patinated copper panels, which often incorporate chameleon-like enamelled silver brooches . **Elizabeth Turrell's** enamel panels, from intimate postcard size to large murals explore various themes from conflict to architecture, employing simple drawing, painting and printmaking approaches in enamel. **Tamar de Vries Winter** fuses ancient and contemporary techniques and concepts to create enamelled jewellery and silverware, including a collection of Judaica.

Studio Fusion Gallery

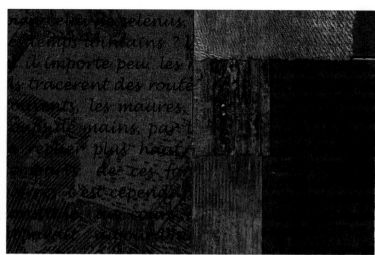

Clockwise from top left:
Elizabeth Turrell – *steel panel*; Gudde Jane
Skyrme – *enamel on copper;*
Joan MacKarrel – *Sea urchin box, silver,
gold foil & enamel*; Tamar de Vries Winter
– *Sterling silver, enamel & gold foil cup,
ht 85mm*; Louise O'Neill – *18ct gold &
tourmaline rings*

Studio Fusion Gallery

Alan Vallis at OXO

209 OXO Tower Wharf, Bargehouse Street
London SE1 9PH
Open: Tuesday-Saturday 11am-6pm

PC

T: 020 7261 9898
E: alan@AlanVallis-OXO.com
www.AlanVallis-oxo.com

Alan Vallis at OXO was one of the first gallery workshops to open at the converted Oxo Tower in 1996 and provides Alan with a central London showcase for his collection of jewellery. The gallery, on the second floor, overlooks the Oxo courtyard where coffee shops provide meeting places for both local business people and visitors wishing to explore the cultural venues of the South Bank.

Alan has redecorated and refitted the gallery space to provide better display areas and a more client friendly space. Some examples of his work are shown on the following pages.

From the left:
* A selection from the 2-D series of wedding bands.
* Two textured wedding bands in 18ct. gold with sapphire and ruby.
* Textured series wedding band and engagement ring with ruby.

Alan Vallis at OXO

Alan Vallis

Stacking Rings are one of Alan's best known ring series. The decorative patterns, textures and colours of the Middle East influenced these rings, which consist of multiple bands worn together, as a group. The two outer bands, form book-ends to the rest of the group, which can be textured, smooth or patterned. Stones can be mounted on the central bands to form a coherent, yet exciting, combination of form colour and pattern.

The latest developments in this series are the Diamond Bridge versions:

Clockwise from the top left:
* Diamond bridge stacking ring with sapphires and princess cut diamonds.
* Gold pendant with diamond and ruby cabochons
* Stacking ring with diamond bridge in platinum with aqua-marine, sapphires and 12pt. diamonds.
* Munich muse necklace with pink Tourmaline.

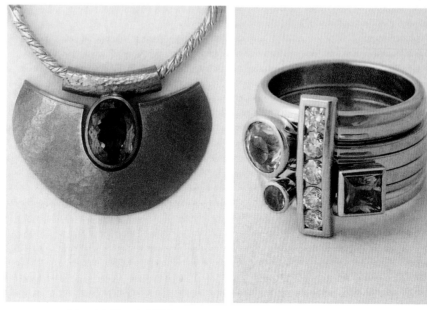

Alan Vallis at OXO

125

Red Biddy Gallery

P C ☕ ♿

7 Kings Road, Shalford
Surrey GU4 8JU
Open: Tuesday-Saturday 10am-6pm

T: 01483 303346
E: info@redbiddygallery.co.uk
www.redbiddygallery.co.uk

Red Biddy Gallery is beautifully situated overlooking the village green in Shalford; one and a half miles south of Guildford on the A281.

This large and airy gallery, opened by Claire and David Longstaff in 2004, continues its ethos of promoting the innovative and unusual alongside established artists. This results in an eclectic and exciting collection which never fails to delight and inspire visitors. A regular programme of mixed and themed exhibitions continues to make this one of Surrey's finest contemporary galleries.

Clockwise from top left:
Craig Carsley – *ceramics ht 50cms;* Phil Vickery – *glass ht 10cms;* Jane Layton – *ceramics ht 20cms;*
Este Macleod – *ceramics ht 30cms;* Paul Jordan – *metal ht 45cms*
Opposite page: Craig Carsley – *ceramic figure ht 45cms*

Red Biddy Gallery

SDC Gallery

24 Rivington Street
London
EC2A 3DU
Open: Please contact the gallery for opening times

T: 020 7613 3886
E: enquiries@sdcgallery.org.uk
www.sdcgallery.org.uk

The newly established SDC gallery is located in the heart of trendy Hoxton just to the east of the City of London.
The aim of the gallery is to showcase the finest crafts produced by the members of the Society of Designer Craftsmen and other prominent designer makers of this country.

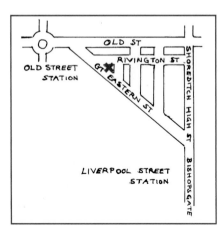

Clockwise from top left:
Carol Naylor – *textiles*; EM Jewellery; Kazumi Harnett – *ceramics*; Cadman – *furniture*

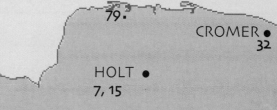

Eastern England

LINCOLN ●

70.

79.

CROMER ●
32

HOLT ●
7, 15

ELY ● 3

CAMBRIDGE ● 28

● OLNEY 85

● MILTON KEYNES 12

Angela Mellor Gallery

38a St Mary's Street, Ely
Cambridgeshire CB7 4ES
Open: Wednesday-Saturday 10:30am-5pm, Sunday 2pm-5pm

T: 01353 666675
E: angela@angelamellorgallery.com
www.angelamellorgallery.com and

International ceramic artist Angela Mellor has now taken over the well established contemporary art gallery, previously run by Ronald Pile, in the historic heart of Ely, 15 miles north of Cambridge.

Situated in a beautifully converted 17th century house close to the cathedral, the light and sophisticated gallery environment on the ground floor now hosts four to six well-researched exhibitions throughout the year.

The programme specialises in showing leading British and International artists as well as local artists' work. The main focus is on ceramics, glass, jewellery and textiles.

Angela Mellor lived in Western Australia for the past 11 years and has been inspired by the landscape, light and coastal environments. Her primary concern has been exploring the light transmitting qualities of bone china.

Clockwise from
top left:
Angela Mellor;
Pippin Drysdale –
porcelain;
Holly Grace –
glass;
Gill Forsbrook –
jewellery;
Sonia Lewis –
porcelain

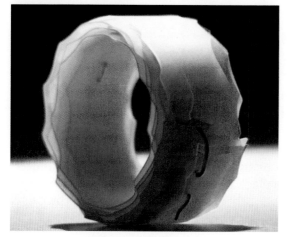

The Appleyard Gallery

P C ☕ ♿

14 The Appleyard, Holt
Norfolk NR25 6AR
Open: Monday-Saturday 10.30am-5pm
(with some seasonal variations)

T: 01263 712315
E: info@theappleyardgallery.co.uk
www.theappleyardgallery.co.uk

The Appleyard Gallery was opened in 2005 in the Georgian market town of Holt. The gallery is a beautiful, open and serene space set in a pretty courtyard in the Appleyard area of restaurants and shops.

Its warm and approachable atmosphere and regularly changing mixed exhibition of Contemporary ceramics, glass, wood, textiles, metals, sculpture, jewellery, accessories, paintings, original prints and photography has earned the gallery a reputation for being the place to go when looking for something original and different for yourself, your home, as a present for another or equally just to view the wonderful work on display.

Clockwise from top left:

Jonathan Trim – *mixed media*; Mandy Walden –– *print;* Alison Wagstaffe – *Fisherman's Friend, print*;
Claire Mallett – *metal;* Shimara Carlow – *jewellery*

artworks-mk

PC ☕ ♿

Great Linford Arts Workshop, Parklands
Great Linford, Milton Keynes
Buckinghamshire MK14 5DZ
Open: Monday-Friday 10am-4pm, Saturday 10am-noon
Closed Sundays and Bank Holidays

T: 01908 608108
E: info@artworks-mk.co.uk
www.artworks-mk.co.uk

artworks-mk is based at Great Linford Arts Workshop, situated in the beautiful surroundings of Great Linford Park in Milton Keynes. The heritage site comprises a 600 year old barn which houses the main exhibition space, coffee bar and general office. Across the courtyard is the Radcliffe building which is home to a large ceramics studio, a fabulous light and airy art room, a 3D workshop with a range of lathes and wood working equipment and a specialist silver-smithing and jewellery studio.

A delightful row of 17th century almshouses provide studio spaces for artists and makers and two pavilions provide further workshop, meeting and studio provision for artists including the Milton Keynes Print Makers.

Photo: George Thompson

artworks-mk have an on going programme of exhibitions, averaging eight – ten per year, showing contemporary craft and art from established and emerging artist/makers. There is a Craft sales area within the coffee bar showing new work every three months.

artworks-mk is an arts education charity and provides a diverse range of artist led activities, workshops and events, throughout the year. Workshops are tailored to suit groups, including schools and community groups but are also suitable for individuals.

Views of the gallery with :
Ruth – *textiles* &
above:
Carla Sealy – *glass bowl*

artworks-mk

Bircham Gallery

14 Market Place, Holt
Norfolk NR25 6BW
Open: Monday-Saturday 9am-5pm
Bank Holidays 10am-4pm

0%

T: 01263 713312
E: birchamgal@aol.com
www.birchamgallery.co.uk

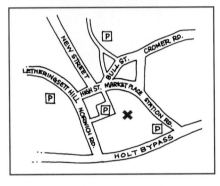

Bircham Gallery is situated in the historic Georgian town of Holt, near the north Norfolk coast. The gallery was established in 1988 by Christopher and Deborah Harrison and has built a reputation for the quality of its artists and exhibitions.

The gallery stocks the work over 200 artists and crafts-people, displaying a wide range of unusual and beautiful art from abstract paintings to kitchen teapots.

Our innovative exhibition programme includes the work of established contemporary artists, acclaimed modern masters and emerging new talent. The artists exhibited at the gallery have been chosen for the quality of their work and imagination. We aim to make viewing and collecting original art an enjoyable and rewarding experience.

136

Bircham Gallery

Clockwise from top left:
Colin See-Payton – *wood-engraving*; Debbie George – *mixed-media painting*;
Kevin Warren – *ceramics*; Karen Atherley – *ceramics*; Donna Barry – *silver & gold*

Cambridge Contemporary Art

P C 0% ♿

6 Trinity Street ,Cambridge CB2 1SU
Open: Monday-Saturday 9am-5.30pm, Sunday 11am-4pm

T: 01223 324222
E: info@cambridgegallery.co.uk
www.cambridgegallery.co.uk

Photo: James Culyer

Cambridge Contemporary Art, established in 1990, is situated in the historic heart of the city. The gallery is set in a spacious 19th century grade 11 listed building and its friendly and welcoming environment provides an ideal place to browse, enjoy and buy the best in contemporary art and craft.

Our constantly changing exhibitions feature sculpture, contemporary paintings, handmade prints, ceramics, glass, wood and metalwork. All the artists are selected on the basis of quality, originality and aesthetic merit. With work by acknowledged masters, established artists and emerging new talent, the gallery has something for everyone. We have built up a reputation for the quality of our artists, the innovation of our shows and the range of our services to collectors. We offer a wedding list service, gift vouchers, interest free credit and in addition to the pieces on display, many of our artists accept commissions.

138

Cambridge Contemporary Art

John Wright

John Wright is a ceramic artist specialising in both hand built and thrown forms. He works with crank and other textural clays and slips combining them with oxidised stoneware glazes.

He is inspired by pebbles, volcanic rocks, sea, lichen, bark and other natural phenomena observed in the landscape of Cornwall and Leicestershire where he is based. Striations of clay and splatters of glaze imitate geological formations and link the pieces.

Grouped together, the pots give a sculptural dimension and playfulness.

Wright is an experimental artist, constantly developing the ceramic forms, giving his work a contemporary edge. There is a strong tactile quality in their matt, rough edges, especially evident in his pebble forms. They are visually stunning; a delight to the senses.

Ann Vernon-Griffiths

"My work is focused on the magic of the material, on form and relationships. It seems to me that glass contains an energy all its own."

Purity of form and a touch of wit characterise Vernon-Griffiths' distinctive pieces of contemporary glassware. Her work is focused on the special qualities of this magical material, capturing the drama and flow of hot glass in the making. Free blown glass jugs, platters, vases, bottles and extraordinary chandeliers express a highly individual style where humour and sophistication meet.

David Robert Carter

David Carter trained originally as a biologist, but turned to metalwork after becoming fired by iron, and in 1986 set up his workshop. He has since gained extensive skills in many areas of metal manipulation including blacksmithing.

Carter experiments with the robust nature of the material and demonstrates a variety of approaches to metal work, from ancient skills to the latest technology. Best known for his range of forged and fabricated candlesticks and candelabrums in a variety of metals and finishes, Carter has recently added to his range with a successful collection of beautifully intricate clocks, as illustrated here.

Helen Martino

Helen Martino combines the discipline of painting and her love of clay in her sculptural ceramics, embellishing the surfaces with layered slips, underglazes and lustres. Martino's Women in Dialogue series show figures in communication with someone unseen, hinting to a dialogue with the viewer. Words are often distorted and disguised within the decoration of the abstracted seat or dresses.

In another series ladies sit in armchairs, sofas, or chaise longues. These have a lighter feeling and are about the pleasures of chatting and gossiping while her figures sitting on cushions are peaceful and meditative in mood.

There is a feminine approach to sculpture in the use of the clay, colour and form that make these very intimate sculptures quietly powerful.

Dan Emmerson

Dan Emmerson began woodturning as a hobby when he was ten and enrolled at a local wood-turning course. His father owned a small sawmill which provided an inspiration, as well as a plentiful supply of unusual timber. Emmerson's fundamental understanding of wood emanates from his selection of thrown bowls and platters, combining the rigid discipline involved in wood-turning while allowing the organic quality of the wood to dictate the form. His range of hand sized apples, pears and eggs have an extremely tactile appeal. Emmerson teaches his profession and gives demonstrations at craft shows up and down the country.

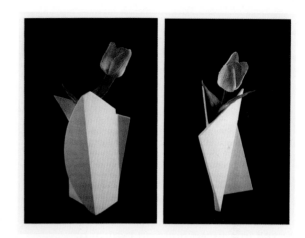

Victoria Dark

Victoria Dark graduated with a BA Hons in Ceramics from Bath Academy of Art and then an MFA from Southern Illinois University. An intensive investigation into Raku has enabled her to develop a real understanding of its complexity and its enormous potential for creating rich, complex surfaces of many overlaid colours and textures.

In her new collection of work, she has designed a series of complex sculptural vases and bowls in porcelain. The vessels are designed so that when viewed from a range of angles, the form is visually different. The distinction between planes is highlighted through variations of whites in satin and gloss glazes. The application varies from subtle scrafitto marks to bold lines that cut through the surface. Dark exhibits extensively in England and America.

Church Street Gallery

3 Church Street, Cromer
Norfolk NR27 9ER
Open: Monday-Saturday 11am-5pm, (closed Wednesdays)
other times by arrangement

T: 01263 510100
E: info@cromerart.co.uk
www.churchstreetgallery.co.uk

Opened in 2004 the Church Street Gallery provides the contemporary art and studio crafts gallery for Cromer and the surrounding area.

Housed in a listed building typical of Cromer's Victorian heritage, the gallery provides a relaxed and friendly setting in which to display work from a selection of artists and makers from throughout the UK. In addition to the gallery sales area there is an exhibition space and regular events feature local and national artists. Work includes ceramics, wood and metal sculpture, glass, jewellery, paintings, original hand produced prints, etchings and collagraphs.

The aim of the owners is to offer something different through the integrity of the work, the consistent quality of selection and through the knowledge of artists gained through relationships built up, often over many years. The predominant theme shares in and celebrates the "Sense of Place" that inspires so many artists in the materials they use and the images they present.

If you are looking for an unusual gift or distinctive item for your home or business then the Church Street Gallery is the place to start.

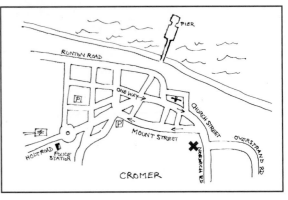

Clockwise from top left:
Kevin Wallhead – *glass*; Walter Awlson – *ceramics*;
Philip Hearsey – *bronze sculpture*; Hazel Atkinson – *jewellery*;
Romey T. Brough – *mono prints*

Church Street Gallery

The Hub

C ☕ 0% ♿

The National Centre for Craft & Design

Navigation Wharf, Carre Street, Sleaford
Lincolnshire NG34 7TW
Open: Daily 10am-5pm

T: 01529 308710
E: hub@leisureconnection.co.uk
www.thehubcentre.org

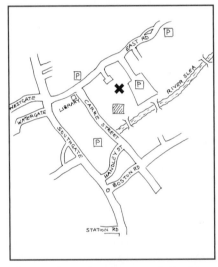

The Hub is the National Centre for craft and design. Converted from an old warehouse it sits most attractively alongside the river Slea, in the market town of Sleaford in Lincolnshire.

The centre offers two gallery spaces, an attractive retail area, a riverside café, teaching rooms and six on-site workshops.

The galleries host up to five major exhibitions a year which explore and display the full range of contemporary craft and design from around the world. Whether functional, decorative or conceptual, visitors are able to view the work of up and coming designers and makers alongside that of established professional crafts-people and designers.

The Hub's wide ranging educational programme offers opportunities for all ages and is increasingly becoming an established part of many local schools outreach curriculum.

The shop affords visitors the perfect opportunity to browse, to marvel and then to purchase. A selection of maker's work is profiled on the following pages.

The Hub

Peter Layton

Peter Layton is a familiar and respected figure in the international glass world. Not just for his work – which has always been innovative and thoughtful, attempting to bridge traditional and contemporary values - but also for his invaluable contribution to the development of the British glass scene. Peter Layton has recently celebrated 30 years of his London Glassblowing Workshop with a nationally touring exhibition.

Jessica Sherriff

Jessica Sherriff lives and works in North Yorkshire. Jessica gained a 1st Class BA Honours degree in Jewellery from Middlesex University in 2003. Her jewellery incorporates natural imagery of Yorkshire countryside, woodland and sky scapes. Using her own photographic material the images are displayed in an original way through a technique of printing onto acrylic. The thickness of acrylic is varied in order to distort the images and allow them to reflect within the shapes themselves; this effect is enhanced by a combination of matt and shiny surfaces.

The Hub

Kei Ito

Kei Ito has developed a sustained practice that spans costume design for dance and theatre companies, textile works, fashion and accessory design. The interrelationship of all these aspects of production tends to create a spiral of influences, across the different varieties of form. Since having an exhibition at Hub in 2001 Kei has had a continual working relationship with the gallery which has given the work constant exposure.

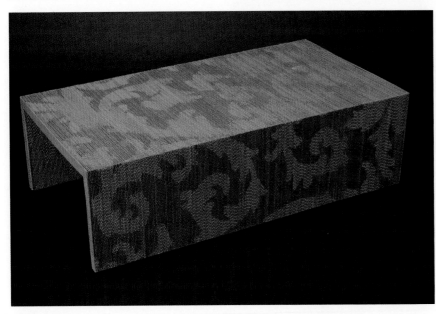

Giles Miller

Giles Miller believes that designers should take a responsibility for the environmental implications of their work, and as a result he has produced collections that incorporate the use of all-natural, recyclable or re-used materials. The Flute collection utilises corrugated cardboard in a way that exploits its corrugation both structurally and aesthetically.

Illustration: *Flute Table*

Wendy Kershaw – 'Ben has only one pair of chopsitcks'
etched on porcelain – page 325

Made in Cley

High Street, Cley-next-the -Sea
Nr Holt, Norfolk NR25 7RF
Open: Monday-Saturday 10am-5pm, Sunday 11am-4pm

c

T: 01263 740134
E: madeincley@aol.com
www.madeincley.co.uk

Made In Cley was established in 1984. Our gallery is on the coast road in the centre of Cley-next-the-Sea on the north Norfolk coast. It is a double fronted Regency shop, which was once the village store. We have transformed it into a high quality contemporary gallery preserving its original features.

We are a group of nine craftspeople and all the work exhibited at Made In Cley is made by us here in our workshops.

Our potters make a full range of functional stoneware pottery. Other members of Made In Cley make and exhibit contemporary jewellery, photographs, prints and sculpture.

Made In Cley Pottery Group

Wolfgang Altmann, Gunhild Espelage, Christiane Guenther, Richard Kelham, Mary Perry, Rosalind Redfern, Nicole Schumacher and Barbara Widdup.

We make a full range of functional stoneware pottery as well as sculptural ceramics, bathroom and kitchen tiles, garden furniture and modern and traditional lighting.
Our pots are ovenproof and dishwasher safe. We also offer a wedding list service.

Quay Proctor-Mears

A ring in silver and gold. Each piece is individually designed and handmade by Quay. She also uses platinum, precious and semi-precious stones, pearls and other materials. Commissions are welcome.

The New Studio

P C ☕ ♿

Rose Court, Olney
Buckinghamshire MK46 4BY
Open: Monday-Saturday 10am-5pm, Sunday 11am-5pm

T: 01234 711994
E: keren@thenewstudio.co.uk
www.thenewstudio.co.uk

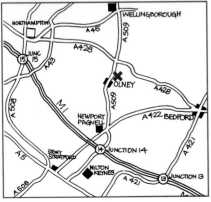

The New Studio opened in 1997 in the thriving market town of Olney. The Studio functions on two floors, each with its own mood: downstairs displays are full of colour and energy while upstairs is a calmer more reflective exhibition space.

A range of media includes ceramics, furniture, sculpture, painting, glass, wood, metal-work, jewellery and textiles.

The New Studio supports and promotes the work of contemporary artists and crafts people at individual and group level, including local Craft Guild members. Exhibitions are staged monthly, with two major exhibitions in June and December each year.

The New Studio

Nina Parker

With an overriding passion for colour and a magpie nature, Nina casts as wide a net as possible to source her eclectic and constantly changing collection of new and vintage glass beads, freshwater pearls and trinkets from around the world.

Incorporating these finds, her aim is always to create unusual yet highly wearable jewellery items. Work style ranges from bold contemporary pieces through to delicate garland necklaces constructed from twisted wire and glass.

Much of her inspiration comes from the gardens hedgerows and coastline around her home in Dorset. Nina loves the capacity that light and colours have to evoke a memory or mood and strives to capture within her jewellery the essence of what she sees.

Richard Forgan

Richard has a natural gift in his perception of form and is inspired by everything around him. He believes his best tool is his open mind that allows him to explore his fascination with form and texture.

His wooden creations are often bold, sculptural pieces that incorporate:
turning, carving, texturing and colouring.

"What attracts and inspires me to work with wood, is the versatility of the medium that allows me to create a form that not only looks right but also feels right".

Ralph Jandrell

Ralph Jandrell grew up in Oswestry, Shropshire and studied fine art degree at Leeds. He then worked at Gwili Pottery near Carmarthen, Wales for five years.

Ralph set up his own studio, Ralph Jandrell Pottery, in 1997 at Coalport China Museum, near Ironbridge, Shropshire. He makes a range of handmade ceramics decorated with his own designs. Each pot is either thrown or cast from a thrown original, and hand painted with liquid clay slips. The pot is then glazed and fired to a high earthenware temperature.

Inspiration for his work comes from the Shropshire countryside- living and working in the Ironbridge Gorge cannot help but inspire an interest in trees!

Paul Barcroft

Confidence and resolution are two words which I feel help to describe my work. As I mature, within this creative discipline, confidence in working through problems becomes greater, a self belief grows, which reflects in the work.

An ability to refer within my personal library of experience enables ideas to formulate which I believe are far more resolved than they were a decade ago.

With some assurance I know my work to have a calmer, mature quality about it. I am comfortable with the current work, considering it to possess special qualities.

Technically I employ sterling silver leaf in several of my designs, others use the materials' properties. Qualities sometimes considered negative are employed to produce stunning surface decorations, although these results are not achieved without the occasional failure. I hope you feel, as I do, the results are worthwhile.

Central England

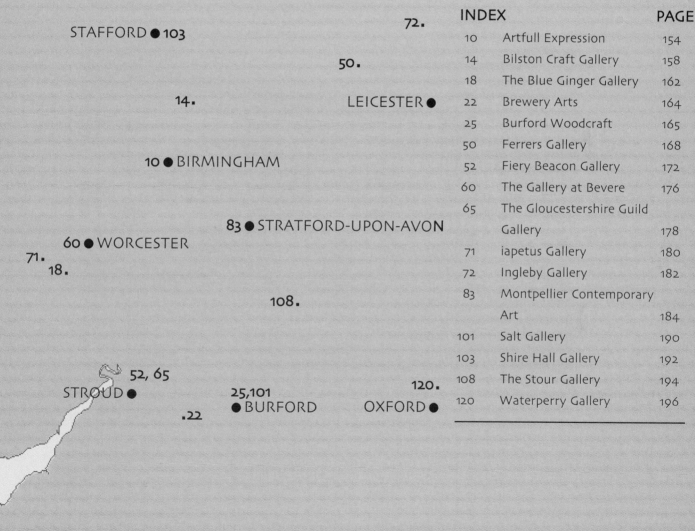

STAFFORD ● 103

72. ▪

50. ▪

14. ▪

LEICESTER ●

10 ● BIRMINGHAM

83 ● STRATFORD-UPON-AVON

60 ● WORCESTER

71. ▪

18. ▪

108. ▪

52, 65

STROUD ●

.22

25,101
● BURFORD

120. ▪

OXFORD ●

Artfull Expression

23/24 Warstone Lane, Hockley, Birmingham B18 6JQ

Open: Monday-Friday 10am-4.30pm and Saturday 10.30am-4.30pm

T: 0121 212 0430

Artfull Expression was opened in a Victorian building in the heart of Birmingham's Jewellery Quarter in 1995 to provide a showcase for contemporary designer-makers in jewellery and other crafts.

It aims to be an alternative to the traditional jewellery shops which surround it. Most of the jewellery it stocks is silver, but – copper, brass, wood, ceramics, plastics and slate are also used.

Some of the jewellers have their workshops in the building. Repairs and commissions can be undertaken. Clocks, mirrors, prints, paintings, small sculptures (in bronze and in ceramics) and greetings cards are also sold.

Artfull Expression was included among the top 50 places to go in *The Independent's* Best of Birmingham 2001 section - a perfect example of the attractions to the discerning shopper of the Jewellery Quarter.

Anna de Ville

Anna de Ville has her workshop in the heart of the Birmingham Jewellery Quarter. She exhibits and sells her work throughout the British Isles.

Her jewellery is distinctive in its use of contrasting oxidised and polished silver, with an emphasis on surface detail. The zig-zag has become a personal motif.

Much of Anna's work is inspired by fish, birds and animals. Her latest designs which include flower and vegetable forms are taken from her beloved garden.

Penny Gildea

Penny Gildea loves the combination of precious metal and glass, the combination of these two materials creates an almost limitless medium of colour and texture on objects that can be functional as well as delicate and decorative.

The traditional techniques of cloisonne, basse taille and champleve show off the relationship between transparent enamels fully and lately she has begun to use handmade kumihimo braids in silk instead of traditional chains to complement the finished pieces.

The range of her work includes jewellery, small objects: bowls and boxes as well as whistles.

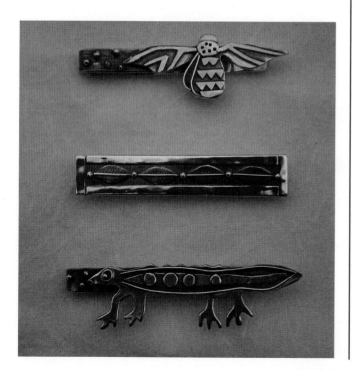

Katherine Campbell-Legg

Katherine Campbell-Legg's work is a subtle combination of silver and 18ct gold, employing a variety of techniques including rolling, stamping, hand-engraving and inlay. She is influenced by natural forms, printed textiles, graphic images and geometrical shapes.

These elements are put together to create wearable contemporary jewellery.

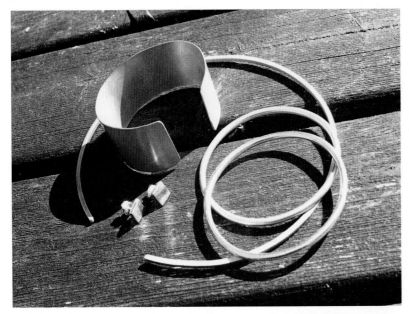

Barbara Quinsey

Barbara Quinsey draws her inspiration from the clean lines and basic forms of abstract modern art, particularly the faceted images of cubism.

Her workshop is located within Birmingham's Jewellery Quarter and she sells her jewellery from a number of retail outlets in the quarter and Birmingham city centre.

Barbara trained in precious metals design at the Birmingham School of Jewellery and has exhibited her work at the Royal Birmingham Society of Artists (RBSA).

Artfull Expression

Michael Turner – stainless steel – pages 23, 227 & 229

Bilston Craft Gallery

P0% ♿

Mount Pleasant, Bilston, Wolverhampton,
West Midlands WV14 7LU
Open: Tuesday & Thursday 10am-4pm,
Wednesday 10am-7pm, Friday 10am-4pm & Saturday 11am-4pm

T: 01902 552507
E: bilstoncraftgallery@dsl.pipex.com
www.wolverhamptonart.org.uk/bilston

From its inception in 1937, Bilston Craft Gallery (then Bilston Museum & Art Gallery) has had a strong local presence, bringing work of national and international quality to the region. In 1999 the Gallery became the designated contemporary craft venue for Wolverhampton Arts and Museums Service and is now the largest publicly funded venue in the West Midlands region to be dedicated to the applied arts.

The Gallery has a lively programme of temporary exhibitions featuring the very best in crafts by national makers, as well as highlighting regional talent. With around five in-house and touring exhibitions a year in the main exhibiting space, the Gallery is fast developing a reputation for showing the finest work from the craft world today.

Craftsense, the permanent exhibition, gives an introduction to craft from the eighteenth century to the present day, and features the nationally renowned Bilston enamels, alongside historical and contemporary items from collections across the country.

Karina Thompson

Multi-sensory work was specially commissioned for Craftsense, with two main objectives: to be something that could be appreciated through touch, sound, smell or even taste; and to be motivated by crafts and materials relevant to this region and its industrial heritage. Birmingham based artist Karina Thompson produced a textile hanging which was inspired by a green miser's purse from our steel jewellery collection.
Illustration:
Miser's Purse, textile hanging

John Grayson

John Grayson produced three enamel boxes in the shape of trifles, based on a significant enamel from our collection - A Trifle from Bilston made in 1790. Since little is known about how the early enamellers worked, John started his pieces from scratch. Each copper base was hammered out by hand and took several weeks to produce.

Illustration: *Trifle from Bilston*

Bilston Community Gallery

Our other exhibiting spaces include First Floor, a community gallery for hire to makers for exhibitions of craft and art, and Craftplay, our award-winning creative play project for pre-school children, which features specially commissioned craft handling pieces. The Gallery also has a beautiful back garden for visitors to enjoy during their visit, with seating and delightful wooden sculptures.

Bilston Craft Shop

High quality functional and decorative pieces are available, to take away on the day, from our craft shop. Work changes seasonally so there is always a special item to suit every taste and pocket, from hand-knitted scarves and leather accessories, to fine silver jewellery and hand-thrown ceramics.

Keep an eye out for the special promotions which we often host at the shop.

Bilston Craft Gallery

Colin See-Payton – wood engraving – page 137

The Blue Ginger Gallery

P C ☕ ♿

Home End Farm, Cradley, Near Malvern
Worcestershire WR13 5NW
Open: Wednesday-Sunday 10am-5.30pm March-December

T: 01886 880240
E: sue@blue-ginger.com
www.blue-ginger.com

The Blue Ginger gallery is distinguished not only by it's carefully selected range of art, crafts and objects of beauty, but also by the attractive location in a converted barn within the grounds of a 16th century former hop farm. Sue Lim, the owner,has an instinct for sourcing things that are infused with pleasure and delight. Among the wide range of creative 'treasures' and continually changing exhibitions you will see that there is a special emphasis given to the strength of local talent. But there is also a strong reflection of Sue's international interests too - the exotic 1970s kimonos brought back from a recent trip to Japan are a good example. Delicious home made food is offered in the cafe, which is set in the relaxed, informal gallery environment that extends into the courtyard during summer months - and B&B is available too. Blue Ginger hosts a variety of craft related courses, workshops and special events, details of which are on the website and regular newsletter. Blue Ginger is easy to find when travelling along the A4103 between Hereford and Worcester, against the backdrop of the glorious Malvern Hills, with easy access from the M5:J7. A visit to Blue Ginger is a treat for the senses!

Clockwise from top left: Chris Poole MBE – *photography*; Diana Arseneau – *jeweller*; Mollie Meager – *glass artist*; Cynthia Lea – *ceramics*; Alice Caroline – *textiles*; Peter Sparrey – ceramics

Brewery Arts

Brewery Court, Cirencester
Gloucestershire GL7 1JH
Open: Monday-Saturday 9.30am-5.30pm, Sundays 10am-4pm

PC ☕ ♿

T: 01285 657181
E: admin@breweryarts.org.uk
www.breweryarts.org.uk

Artist: Nigel Shute

Brewery Arts, Cirencester is situated in a vibrant market town in the heart of the Cotswolds.
The Craft Shop is known locally and nationally as a centre of excellence for the work it shows. A wide selection of ceramics, papier-mâché, metalwork, jewellery and glass is on display in this Aladdin's cave of inspiration. In 2007 the Victorian brewery buildings under went a major refurbishment funded by the Arts Council of England, local government, Trusts and donations allowing better access and improved facilities. The Craft Shop and award winning Craftworkers   continued to be open to the public in the Brewery Arts Theatre. The refurbished centre reopens with a comprehensive education programme, an exhibition space, Craft Shop and Coffee-house and extended opening hours. We have 15 on site Craftworkers including a glass workshop, jeweller and textile artists.

   At the time of going to press the refurbishment is on going please follow our progress on the website or phone to receive an update if you intend to make a special journey

Burford Woodcraft

P C

144 High Street, Burford, Oxon OX18 4QU
Open: Monday-Saturday 9.30am-5pm
Sunday 11am-4.45pm mid February-December

T: 01993 823479
E: enquiries@burford-woodcraft.co.uk
www.burford-woodcraft.co.uk

Burford Woodcraft looks down the High Street, through the listed architecture characteristic of the Cotswolds, towards the River Windrush. Here it continues to be one of Britain's leading craft galleries specialising in contemporary woodwork.

A welcoming and informal atmosphere allows visitors and makers to share their passion whilst introducing new friends to the natural beauty, diversity and tactile quality of wood. Each of the designer makers understands and combines these qualities with a superb standard of craftsmanship, versatility and individuality, to achieve the best possible. The continuously evolving collection is chosen carefully with attention to detail by Robert and Jayne Lewin to offer innovative, practical and humorous pieces that are affordable and value for money. Robert is one of the individual designer-makers whose furniture and mirrors are featured alongside the other work, handmade in Britain. The impressive range includes furniture, unusual puzzles and clocks; creative sculptures and one-off pieces, practical but interesting kitchenware, desk accessories, jewellery boxes and much more. All created with inspiration and lovingly made from a very natural medium.

Robert Lewin

I design and make contemporary furniture to commission and one off and limited edition pieces, for sale in the gallery and exhibitions. A Shaker influence is often evident in simple lines which highlight the grain of the wood.

British hardwoods are sourced locally whenever possible but occasionally North American timbers are used with some exotics for contrasting panels and handles. All are from sustainable supplies. I finish pieces with natural oils to nourish and release the beauty held within the wood.

My furniture is complemented with smaller items that I produce exclusively for Burford Woodcraft, such as mirrors and photograph frames, which feature inlays or wany edged burr woods.

Alec Garner

Alec Garner has had a passion for working with wood since childhood and after gaining a qualification in Furniture Design & Construction, realised his aspirations by setting up his own workshop supplying the occasional piece of bespoke furniture but mainly handcrafted boxes.

Most of the timber Alec uses is sourced locally, but some of his designs incorporate exotic woods, as many of these are highly figured or naturally brightly coloured and add striking contrasts to native species.

The inspiration for his designs comes from the beauty of the wood itself and the complexity of grain patterns, composition and colours. The final finishing process is where the figuring and hidden depths of the woods are fully exposed and this is the process that he feels makes all the hard bench work so rewarding.

Philippine Sowerby

I make two and three-dimensional wooden jigsaw puzzles, each cut from a single piece of local hardwood and finished to show the wood's natural beauty; over time they have got harder for me to make and for you to complete.

The puzzles are tactile sculptures to enjoy for their beauty; they are pieces of art for grown ups to play and have fun with.

Colin Gosden

Combinations of form and texture are the motivation behind most of my work. I like timber which has acquired character through natural processes, and I often combine this with sound material to achieve both visual and tactile interest. I also use colour, applied in opaque form or in layered glazes to extend the potential of the medium.

Off centre turning plays a major role in my working methods, this enables me to explore feelings of movement and motion, which are strong recurrent themes. Some forms are static, but others are designed to be unstable, this allows them to move if disturbed. When at rest, these pieces settle asymmetrically due to uneven distribution of weight.

My clock designs, which employ construction and composition techniques, are informed by the same principles as the rest of my work.

Ferrers Gallery

Ferrers Centre for Arts and Crafts
Staunton Harold, Ashby de la Zouch
Leics. LE65 1RU
Open: Tuesday-Sunday 11am-5pm, closed Mondays

P C ☕ ♿
T: 01332 863337
E: info@ferrersgallery.co.uk
www.ferrersgallery.co.uk

The multi award winning Ferrers Gallery promotes the very best in British contemporary craft and design. Situated in the tranquil valley of Staunton Harold at the heart of the National Forest, the gallery nestles in the courtyard of the Ferrers Centre for Arts and Crafts, home to numerous craft studios and tea room.

The Ferrers Gallery has three floors of jewellery, textiles, glass, ceramics, metalwork and paintings, it hosts two year round exhibition programmes and also runs marketing courses for visual artists and crafts-people. Stunning scenery with permitted pathways past Staunton Harold Hall, lake and National Trust church surrounds the Ferrers Gallery making it a relaxing and enjoyable visit.

'Lovely refreshing contemporary ideas. A pleasure to look around"

"Amazed at the creativity, skill and ingenuity – great'

'Absolutely wonderful, antiques of the future'

'My children said there was something fantastic upstairs- they were right!'

168

Stephanie Bowen

Stephanie Bowen designs and makes contemporary fused glass at her company Morpheus Glass. She uses layers of vivid colours and lively surface textures to create depth and character to each individual piece. Working from her Lancashire based studio Stephanie combines glass powders, coloured grains, precious metals and metal oxides to produce the incredible effects between the layers of her work. Pieces include small to large scale wall art, functional vessels, splash backs, wall tiles and polished glass jewellery. Commissions welcome.

LoCo Glass

Colin and Louise Hawkins have been designing and blowing glass in partnership since 1998, they continue to explore and be inspired by the glass itself, its qualities as a medium and the processes involved in manipulating it to achieve texture and form, endeavouring to produce work that combines quality craftsmanship with contemporary design.

With a characteristic use of strong simple shapes and an individual approach to traditional glass making techniques they have developed a broad range of work that is exhibited widely in the UK and abroad.

Lisa Watson

Lisa intends the wearer to be able to relate to the ideas and notions expressed in her pieces in such a way that inspires the recollection of feelings and memories, such as sitting in a field or a garden, picking flowers and making daisy chains. Ultimately, she hopes her jewellery allows the wearer to recall the experiences of childhood.

Her existing range centres upon flowers, using silver with gold details, and also incorporating anodised aluminium, giving colour to the pieces. Her work also has a playful, witty dimension. Although pieces should be worn, they should be viewed as miniature pieces of sculpture when they are not.

Oliver Vowles-Burrows & Pamela Burrows

Pamela Burrows studied sculpture at Camberwell College of Art, London, and then trained with Designer/Jeweller Christopher Burrows. Oliver Vowles-Burrows, their son, studied art and design at Falmouth School of Art. After a period in a design studio, he decided to specialise in jewellery making and design, upon realising this was an inherent strength.

Oliver and Pamela work from their studio close to some of the wildest coastline in North Cornwall, where the form and structure of their work echoes the boldness of the rugged landscape. Their work shows an interest in sculptural themes, using shape and colour in an abstract balance to create individual pieces. They work using 9ct and 18ct gold, with precious and semi-precious stones, many of which are sourced by Oliver and Pamela in India and Sri Lanka for their special qualities.

Ferrers Gallery

Blandine Anderson

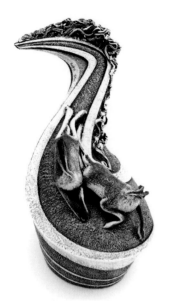

The inspiration for Blandine's stoneware and porcelain work begins in the landscape of North Devon. The scale captures both the broad sweep of open fields and the minutiae of hedgerows. The colours are directly affected by the changing seasons.
Recent works explore simpler, sculptural themes, emphasising form and texture. These are inspired by the shapes of natural found objects.

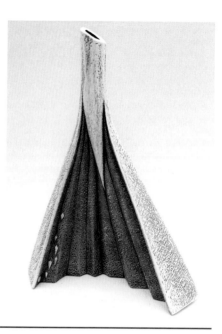

From the left:
Darren Dearden – *painting;*
Glacier Glass & Duncan Thurlby – *metal*

Fiery Beacon Gallery

New Street, Painswick GL6 6UN
Open: Friday-Saturday 10am-6pm
Sunday noon-5pm, Bank Holiday Monday 10am-6pm
Closed January, February, September, October

T: 01452 812582
E: gallery@fierybeacon.co.uk
www.fierybeacon.co.uk

Set in the attractive Cotswold village of Painswick the Fiery Beacon Gallery has long been a focus for art and crafts. Today you will find a regularly changing display which focuses on a number of individuals or themes. Occupying the ground floor of the owner's Cotswold stone grade II listed building the traditional architecture is an ideal foil for the exciting collection of contemporary work.

The gallery aims to show the work of both new and well established artists working in glass, ceramics and metal, together with an unusual collection of jewellery and hand made cards.

While in the village take time for a stroll and visit the 11th century church with its famous yew trees, explore the Rococo gardens on the outskirts of the village and don't miss the other interesting shops.

Fiery Beacon Gallery

Michael Peckitt

This established designer never makes the same piece twice. We appreciate the originality of his very colourful jewellery. Working in anodised aluminium the jewellery takes on the mantle of dynamic wearable art.

Lynn Walters

I am a designer maker of metal and wire sculpture. My work is inspired by memories of people and places. Vibrant street scenes are evocative of any place where people inhabit. Coloured houses represent their occupants, giving each individual house a personality. Figures are walking, playing, sitting on benches and walking their dogs along winding pathways surrounded by flowers and fences......

Fiery Beacon Gallery

Clockwise from top left:
LoCo Glass; Sarah Jane Brown –
metal sculptures; Penny Williams –
metal; Janet O'Donnell – *textiles*;
Rob Whelpton – *ceramics*

Fiery Beacon Gallery

Clockwise from top left:
Elizabeth Hinton – *jewellery*; Pauline
Zelinski – *ceramics*; Michelle Ohlson –
ceramics; Tracey Grist – *glass*;
Margaret Johnson – *glass*

The Gallery at Bevere

P C ☕

Bevere Lane
Worcester WR3 7RQ
*Open: Tuesday–Saturday and the first Sunday of
the month 10.30am–5pm or by appointment at any other time*

T: 01905 754 484
E: enquiries@beverevivis.com
www.beverevivis.com

'The Gallery at Bevere shows the best of modern British studio ceramics, along with paintings and other crafts in an intimate setting. A regional gallery, showing national artists'
David Whiting, Ceramics Critic

The Gallery at Bevere is a major centre for the visual arts, offering high quality exhibitions and sale of the work of top nationally known artists, glassmakers, wood-turners and ceramicists

In our two main galleries we have eight exhibitions a year with featured makers and artists, whilst the showcase room houses examples of work by exhibitors past and future. We have a wide range of outdoor ceramics and sculptures in our courtyard and the grounds surrounding the gallery. We also stock etchings, prints, woodcuts and a range of art and craft books, cards and

magazines for sale

We have plenty of free parking outside the gallery and picture framing workshop and are wheelchair friendly with ramps or very small steps into

the exhibitions. There is no admission charge and refreshments are served from the Gallery Café open April to September inclusive.

Clockwise from top left:
Karinna Sellars – *blown & hand-formed glass*;
Claudia Lis & John Pollex – *ceramics*; Mark Hancock
– *wood*; Walter Keeler – *earthenware*

The Gallery at Bevere

The Gloucestershire Guild Gallery

P C

T: 01452 814745
E: info@guildcrafts.org.uk
www.guildcrafts.org.uk

Painswick Centre, Bisley Street, Painswick
Gloucestershire GL6 6QQ
Open: Tuesday-Saturday 10 am–5 pm, some seasonal opening variations

The Gloucestershire Guild of Craftsmen was founded in 1933 with direct links to the Cotswold Arts and Crafts movement. Now a registered charity the Guild has continued to develop as an association of professional craftspeople.

Through its selection process, the Guild continues its pursuit of excellence in contemporary craft. Applicants are selected to become an Associate Member for two years, after which time the Guild elects Associates to Full Membership.

The Guild's permanent Gallery was established in Painswick in 2000. A changing selection of contemporary collectable work by Guild members is shown all year round including ceramics, jewellery, glass, wood, paper, furniture and much more.

The Guild also holds at least

two exhibitions a year in venues around Gloucestershire and Guild members regularly hold workshops throughout the county.

The new Guild films Made for You 1 and 2 are on sale on DVD in the Gallery. They give an inspiring insight into a group of Guild members demonstrating their craft and talking about their work.

The Gloucestershire Guild Gallery

Clockwise from top left:
Jan Bunyan – *potter*; Brian Jordan – *furniture*; Jenny Ford – *textiles*;
William Robson – *glass*; Fionna Hesketh – *jewellery*

The Gloucestershire Guild Gallery

iapetus Gallery

P C ♿

32 Belle Vue Terrace
Great Malvern,
Worcestershire WR14 4PZ
Open all year: Monday-Saturday 10am-5.30pm

T: 01684 566929
E: info@iapetus.co.uk
www.iapetus.co.uk

iapetus gallery opened in 2005 when we transformed an unloved Victorian shop into a Mecca for jewellery magpies, eccentrics and ladies-what-lunch!

The idea behind iapetus is pretty simple – we sell things you'll really want, and none of that boring stuff you actually need (but hey when you want it, you need it!) We offer a tempting collection of handmade jewellery, glass, ceramics and gifts which aren't afraid to stand out from the crowd. Our artists' work is crafted with love, skill and ingenuity, mixed with a dose of quirkiness.

Iapetus Gallery shows the work of over 75 British and International artists, including Kosta Boda's delicious collection of handmade glass from Sweden, and the innovative designs of the Deco Echo group of Polish jewellers. We love to support local artists too, and much of our collection doesn't travel far to reach us.

Can't make it to see us, or want to have a nosy round before you make the journey? Why not pop along to www.iapetus.co.uk you'll find a great selection of our work and you can even do a spot of online shopping!

iapetus
g a l l e r y
love life's little luxuries

Clockwise from top left:
Harriet Bedford – *jeweller*;
Bronwyn Tyler-Jones – *metal*;
Bertil Vallien – *glass*;
Adele Taylor – *kaleidoscopes*;
James Newman – *jeweller*

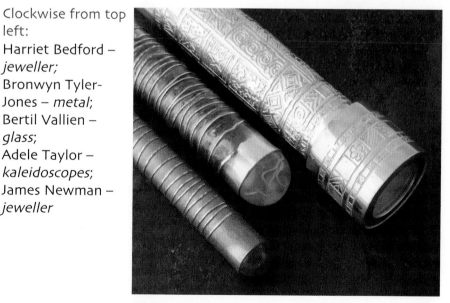

Ingleby Gallery

P C

Ingleby, Melbourne, Derby DE73 7HW
Open: during exhibitions Wednesday-Friday 10am-4pm
Saturday and Sunday 12noon-5pm

T: 01332 865995
E: gillwatson@ingleby-gallery.co.uk
www.ingleby-gallery.co.uk

Ingleby Gallery sits gently in the Trent Valley surrounded by open pasture land extending to the river with ponds and ducks, a very rural setting with ample parking for visitors.

The brick building housing the Gallery was originally a shire horse stable, part of one of the working farms on Sir Francis Burdett's Foremarke Estate. Built in the 18th century it still has many of its original features, including hayrack and harness pegs. The Gallery is open for set two week exhibitions through-out the year featuring both contemporary and traditional artists except at Christmas when the special exhibition is a month long. The ever changing collection of paintings, quality jewellery, ceramics, bronze sculpture, metalwork and glass - ware is produced by talented artists and crafts people.

The Gallery aims to provide a fascinating mix of diverse styles and skills with a welcoming vibrant atmosphere. The gallery website provides the programme details for the year.

Clockwise from top left: Anuk Naumann – *mixed media;*
Sue Riley – *bronze resin (also torso on opposite page);*
Thomas Petit – *glass;* Julie Wilson – *stoneware*

Ingleby Gallery

183

Montpellier Contemporary Art C 0% ♿

8 Chapel Street
Stratford-upon-Avon, CV37 6EP
Open: Monday-Saturday 9.30am-5.30pm

T: 01789 261161
E: info@montpelliergallery.com
www.montpelliergallery.com

Montpellier Gallery has been established in the heart of Stratford-upon-Avon since 1991, and can be found opposite the Shakespeare Hotel near the centre of the town. Set in a 400 year old building, the gallery comprises three adjoining rooms, opening to a delightful tiny courtyard, which floods the rooms with natural light.

We have built a strong reputation for the broad selection of contemporary works we show, giving the gallery its visual excitement, colour and a refreshing stylistic diversity – whether ceramics, studio glass, paintings, printmaking or contemporary jewellery, pieces are always selected using a discerning eye for their quality, originality and form. We are strongly committed to promoting an awareness of the hand-made process and originality in all media. The gallery always carries a comprehensive range of pieces from the artists and craftsmen we represent and regularly feature solo or group exhibitions by new and established makers.

The Gallery is run by Peter Burridge, a trained jeweller/silversmith and printmaker, bringing his broad knowledge of the Fine Arts and Crafts to create the Gallery's breadth of choice and selection. We are a member of the Independent Craft Galleries Association, and regularly judge for the Giftware Association and British Jewellers Association. We also have a number of long-established relationships with artists from France and Italy.

Elaine Peto

Elaine strives to capture the character and energy of each creature she makes, bestowing upon them their own individual personality. After graduating from Exeter in 1985 she continued to study livestock at agricultural markets and abattoirs to develop her understanding of animal anatomy and movement. Each sculpture she produces is individually made using rolled and highly textured clay sheets. After gently constructing, modelling and applying subtle details to the form she then adds oxides and glazes to the surface, before finally firing to stoneware in her kiln. She says she is often amazed at how the material seems to take on a life of its own, imparting its own particular spirit to the finished piece.

Peter Eugene Ball

Peter Eugene Ball works with found objects, natural materials and artifacts - a piece of dramatically eroded driftwood, a shell, a cluster of old brass cow bells. These objects not only provide the materials but also the stimulus for his sculpture. He handles this material intuitively, projecting onto it the images drawn from such influences as prehistoric, Romanesque and medieval art and architecture. Peter was born in Warwickshire in 1943, and studied at Coventry College of Art. His work can be seen in many of the most important churches and cathedrals throughout England and Wales Including Southwell Minster, Winchester, Portsmouth and Birmingham Cathedral, as well as in numerous private collections both here, Europe and the U.S.A.

Paul Finch

Paul specialises in designing and making contemporary jewellery in silver, 18ct gold and other precious metals. He has been working as a self-taught designer jeweller since 1998 and is based in Cornwall. His jewellery is unusual and created for the individual, having durability and comfort as a priority. His Trap and Wiggle ranges show his evident skill in designing pieces that hold the precious stones he uses to their best advantage, creating pieces that are made for wearing, both practical and elegant.

Mackay & Pearson

Fiona Mackay and David Pearson have been making jewellery since 1979. They have been well established in their own workshop in Harbury, West Yorkshire since 1996 where they design and produce a wide diversity of precious, individually crafted pieces. Originally trained at Sheffield, Fiona is the creative inspiration behind many of the ranges, having worked for many years as an independent designer for larger companies. Their work now shows a wonderful elegance of line, and incorporates coloured, precious and semi-precious stones. Recently, the addition of subtle jades and bright corals have been incorporated into the pieces they make.

Rob Whelpton

Rob Whelpton's distinctive ceramics are created by the Raku process and are fired outdoors. The characteristic crackling of the glazes and glowing colours of this method are achieved by placing the red hot pots in sawdust, which ignite with the heat, further charring the unglazed areas. The combinations and textures this creates are as effective as they are unexpected. His stylised designs incised on the surface of the pots incorporate birds, animals, boats and fish motifs, used in rhythmic and intertwining shapes, with much beauty and a certain humour. They are distinctively coloured using slips and metallic salts, some pots are further enhanced using gold leaf. Most recently people have become a strong feature in his designs.

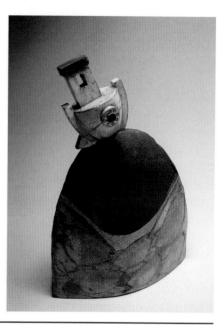

Stuart Akroyd

After graduating from Sunderland Polytechnic in 1988, Stuart worked at the International Glass Centre, Brierley Hill, and then as head production designer-maker at a factory in the Lake District. In 1991 he returned to Sunderland to teach glass-making at the University and set up his own studio. Today his work is fresh and confident, specialising in stunningly pure, asymmetrical designs executed in a wide range of vibrant colours and often inspired by natural forms. The cold working techniques introduced over the years - which include carving and polishing - give the surfaces of his pieces a wonderful pattern and movement, often with intriguing optical effects. Stuarts' work is represented by many leading galleries and larger more complex pieces can be seen in many private collections.

John Mainwaring

From boyhood, wood and art seem to have been an intrinsic part of John's life. He received private tuition in art after leaving school, leading him to become a cartoonist in the commercial world, before turning back to his love of wood in the early 70s.

John likes to work quickly and instinctively with his hands and think with his heart. With carving there is always the risk of failure, but usually the excitement of getting it right which can be tremendously satisfying and rewarding. His love of wildlife in all its forms, is strongly evident in his work, but he now experiments with more elaborate, one-off pieces, often referring to his cartoons for inspiration that involve piety, humour and John's particular sense of fun.

From the left: Annie Peaker;
Selected glass makers &
Paul Barcroft

Montpellier Contemporary Art

Left: Richard Wilson –
ceramics
Right: Peter Eugene Ball
– *sculpture*

Montpellier Contemporary Art

Salt Gallery

P ♿

4 Bear Court, 38 Lower High Street
Burford, Oxfordshire OX18 4RR
Open: Daily 10am-5pm

T: 01993 822371
E: sales@saltgallery.com
www.saltgallery.com

The Salt Gallery, in Burford's picturesque Cotswold stone courtyard of Bear Court, specialises in the sale of British studio pottery and glass from some of the UK's leading potters and glassmakers. The space occupied by the gallery is surprisingly light, benefiting from three sunny cottage windows and items are displayed in an uncluttered way.

The gallery caters for both the serious collector and the casual visitor. It always has a wide selection of salt glaze work, especially the highly praised work of Steve Harrison and ceramics by the likes of John Leach, Andrew Hill, Alistair Young and others as well as sculptural pieces by Janet Halligan and Libby Edmondson. This is complemented by an extensive range of studio glass, in particular glass by Norman Stuart Clarke and Lesley Clarke, Will Shakspeare, Tom Petit, Karinna Sellars, Andrew Potter, Rebecca Morgan and Sanders & Wallace. All work is signed and often dated by the maker. The gallery likes to offer a good selection in design and price.

We also have a selection of paintings from the Wren Gallery of Burford these may be viewed on a separate website www.wrenfineart.com.

Steve Harrison

Steve Harrison is a studio potter with a particular gift for taking historical techniques and bringing them up to date. He trained for seven years, concluding at the Royal College of Art in 1993. Steve makes individual salt glazed utilitarian pots, including tea pots, mugs, jugs and bowls. Each one is different but unmistakably of the one family.

His finely thrown, innovative work is in a process of continuous evolution. His kiln has matured to the point that each firing marks a new stage in the works development. The form, function and aesthetic significance of the work places it in the context of today – progressive and challenging.

We maintain a stock of Steve's work at all times, all work is date stamped making it an ideal special present. A joy to own, a joy to use!

From the left: Lesley Clarke; Libby Edmondson & Norman Stuart Clarke

Salt Gallery

Shire Hall Gallery

Market Square
Stafford, ST16 2LD
Open: Monday-Saturday 9.30am-5pm,
Tuesday 9.30am-5pm & Sunday 1pm-4pm

☕ **0%** ♿
T: 01785 278345
E: shirehallgallery@staffordshire.gov.uk
www.staffordshire.gov.uk/sams

At the Shire Hall Gallery our aim is to inspire, stimulate and sometimes challenge you by providing a constantly changing exhibition programme featuring a wide variety of subjects, artists and styles of art.

The Craft Shop represents many leading British crafts-people, showing high quality contemporary craft. We stock a wide range of ceramics, textiles, jewellery, wood and glass work - and a large selection of greetings cards and wrap.

The Gallery now offers a Multi-Sensory room which allows visitors to experience different light, sound and tactile sensations. This room is available for everyone but we hope that it will be of particular interest to visitors with physical, visual and hearing impairments.

Why not try the Balcony

Coffee Bar where you can relax and enjoy a view over the Great Hall with a superb collection of teas, coffees, cakes and savouries.

*Level access from the street
*Chairlift to the Courtroom
 (limited access) & coffee bar.
*Accessible toilets with
 baby- changing facilities.
*Induction loop system in main
 gallery spaces.
*Guide/hearing dogs are welcome

Shire Hall Gallery

Clockwise from top left:
Yu Lan Burkmar; Tracy Birchwood; Louise Thompson & Twists Glass

The Stour Gallery

P 0%

10 High Street, Shipston-on-Stour
Warwickshire CV36 4AJ
Open: Monday-Saturday 10am-5.30pm

T: 01608 664411
E: info@thestourgallery.co.uk
www.thestourgallery.co.uk

The Stour Gallery is a three-story building of white spaces and courtyard garden showing contemporary art in the market town of Shipston-on-Stour, situated on the Oxfordshire, Gloucestershire and Warwickshire borders; successfully showing the work of painters, printmakers, sculptors, potters and jewellers with established reputations alongside emerging artists, with equal commitment to both. There is a particular emphasis on Cornish and West Country work, especially from the Penwyth and Newlyn Societies, and increasingly fine and applied art from Ireland.

Established in 1997 the gallery's continued and growing success is due to the very high standard, originality and coherence of the work it shows. A series of changing exhibitions and work by gallery artists always being available – ensures

Photo: Louise Darby

that visits will be rewardingly varied. You are welcome to visit simply to enjoy the work.

Please contact the gallery to go on our mailing list – exclusive gallery use.

Gallery applied artists include:
Potters: Andrews, Batterham, Beard, Blandino, Carter, Doherty, Conrad, Darby, Hake, James, Jelfs, Keeney, Leach, Malone, Maltby, Perryman, Rich, Hall, Underhill, Ward, Welch, Wheeler.
Sculptors: Buck, Hayes, Higgins, MacLeod, Maiden, Marvell, Sinclair.
Jewellers: Adam, Christie, Cowen.

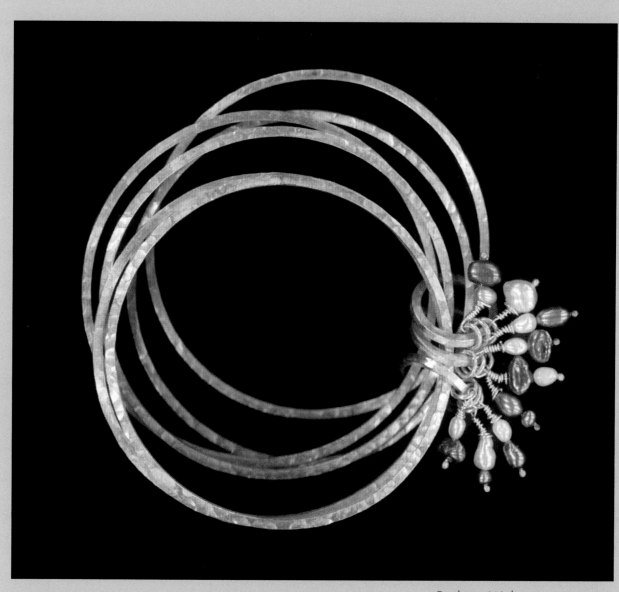

Barbara Webster – page 297

Editor's Choice

Waterperry Gallery

P ☕ ♿

Waterperry, Near Wheatley
Oxfordshire OX33 1JZ
Open: Tuesday-Sunday, (open bank holidays)
April-October 10am-5pm , Nov-March 10.am-4.30pm

T: 01844 338085
E: gallery@waterperrygardens.co.uk
www.waterperrygardens.co.uk

Housed in the grounds of this beautiful country estate, the Waterperry Gallery sources and supports both established and emerging UK-based artists.

With the focus very much on original, dynamic works of art, you'll find plenty of creative ideas in the sympathetically restored 18th century barn.

This inspirational setting provides the perfect backdrop for the many articles of fine craftsmanship and quality, among them collections of ceramics, jewellery, sculpture and textiles which are constantly changed to provide interest however often you may visit.

Don't miss Art in Action every July, when more than

250 artists take over the estate for four days, offering visitors the chance to learn more about - and have a try - at all the different artistic disciplines.

Just 40 minutes from London on the outskirts of Oxford, Waterperry also offers the chance to visit our eight-acre ornamental garden, plant centre, teashop, Saxon Church and Museum of Rural Life.

Clockwise from top left:
Ladies Who Lunch;
Jennifer Hall;
David Aylesbury;
Daren Greenhow – *metal*;
John Hine

Waterperry Gallery

Cockerell & Son – paper – page 99

Editor's Choice

Midwest & Wales

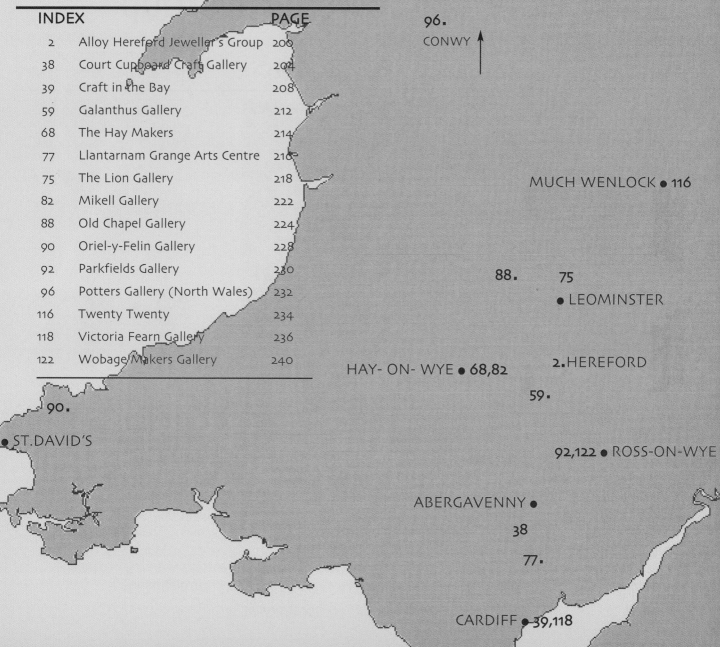

96.
CONWY

MUCH WENLOCK ● 116

88.   75

● LEOMINSTER

HAY- ON- WYE ● 68,82   2.HEREFORD

59.

90.

● ST.DAVID'S

92,122 ● ROSS-ON-WYE

ABERGAVENNY ●

38

77.

CARDIFF ● 39,118

Alloy Hereford Jeweller's Group

The Courtyard, Edgar Street
Hereford HR4 9JR
Open: Monday-Saturday 10am-7pm

P C ☕ 0% ♿

T: 01432 279144
E: shows@alloyjewellers.org.uk
www.alloyjewellers.org.uk

Top – Georgina Franklin
Shirley Smith

Alloy are a professional group of designer jewellers, silver-smiths and metalworkers. Established in 1993, the group provides support for makers based in Herefordshire, and co-ordinates exhibitions and projects in the West Midlands and beyond. In 1998, the group was awarded funding from the National Lottery to build a purpose built jewellery work-shop at The Courtyard Arts Centre in Hereford.

Alloy now also has three permanent showcases in the foyer of The Courtyard, featuring seasonal exhibitions of members work, alongside educational and spotlight displays. They also present work by West Midlands Artists working in other craft disciplines.

Alloy Hereford Jeweller's Group

Clockwise from top left: Bev Milward – *porcelain;* Bronwen Tyler-Jones – *silver & non-precious metals;* Helen Brice – *9ct yellow gold & coloured resin;* Carole Leonard – *perspex & silver*

Clockwise from top left:
Rebecca Lewis – *pearls, agate & silver;*
Louise Chesshire – *silver;*
Will Evans – *precious metals & gems;*
Rozie Keogh – *wirework*

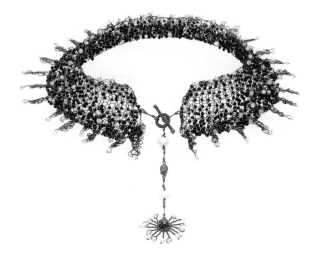

Lynsey Walters – felt – page 268

Court Cupboard Craft Gallery

PC ☕ ♿

New Court Farm
Llantilio Pertholey
Abergavenny Monmouthshire NP7 8AU
Open: Daily 10.30am-5.pm.

T: 01873 852011
E: blackmntncircle@btconnect.com
www.courtcupboardgallery.com

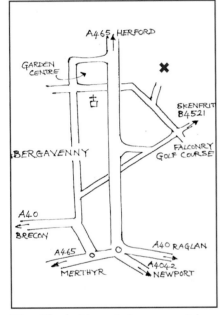

The Black Mountains are set in the Brecon Beacons National Park, an area much appreciated by visitors all over the world. The Court Cupboard Craft Gallery is situated on the western slopes of the Skirrid Mountain close to the market town of Abergavenny and near castles, a golf course and falconry centre.

The Gallery is run by members of The Black Mountains Circle, who draw inspiration for their designs from the location in which they live and work.

A comprehensive selection of high quality, collectable work is available throughout the year. Some members welcome visitors to their studios by prior arrangement and all accept commissions. A comfortable coffee shop offers a variety of refreshments and locally made cakes. There is free parking and a washroom for the disabled.

Court Cupboard Craft Gallery

Sioni Rhys Handweavers

In a district famous for its soft flannel, the craft of weaving continues in the studios of Sioni Rhys Handweavers. The traditional Carthen or throw is woven in the modern idiom with pure new wool, reflecting the colours of the surrounding Black Mountains. The Celtic inspiration in the textiles is evident in the new Llanofer Heritage range of throws which echo the traditional weaves of the mills of the area.

Fashion accessories in luxury fibres are also created by designer and weaver, using age old methods to produce textiles with soft handle and good drape.
www.sioni-rhys-handweavers.com.

Frances Lester

Frances Lester trained as a jeweller in her late 40's after a career as an engineer. A sense of structure and balance are part of her design personality and have common ground with her former career and with her jewellery designs.

The designs are inspired by a particular event, from her studies of fluid dynamics or from her hobbies of sailing, rowing and swimming. They pass through the sketch book, but are finally resolved in the round. In her case hand made is a particularly appropriate description because she uses mainly her fingers to create the lines of her work.

David Haswell

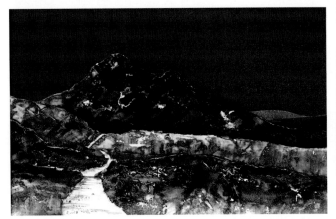

Highly textured images of the Welsh landscape painted in mixed media. Available as originals or fine art quality limited edition giclée prints in a variety of sizes.

E: haswelldavid@aol.com

Court Cupboard Craft Gallery

Phil Vickery – glass – page 127

Craft in the Bay

The Flourish, Lloyd George Avenue
Cardiff Bay CF10 4QH
Open: Daily 10.30am-5.30pm

P C ☕ %/% ♿

T: 02920 484611
E: mgw@craftinwales.com
www.makersguildinwales.org.uk

Craft in the Bay is the home of Wales' leading craft association: the Makers Guild of Wales.

Housed in a refurbished and extended dockside transit shed – though now mainly of glass – it stands immediately opposite the Wales Millennium Centre in Cardiff Bay.

The Guild is dedicated to showing Welsh craft at its finest, and members' work is displayed alongside changing exhibitions of craft of international repute from beyond Wales, in the 4000 sq.ft. gallery space. There are also teaching workshops, a conference room and café.

Craft in the Bay is run co-operatively by Guild members whose carefully selected work includes textiles, ceramics, jewellery, wood, glass, metal, leather and basketry.

How to find us:
From the west: leave the M4 at Junction 33, follow A4232 to Cardiff Bay.
From the east: leave M4 at Junction 29, take 3rd exit off A48, follow signs to Cardiff Bay.
Nearest parking at Mermaid Quay and the Red Dragon Centre.

Lynn Walters

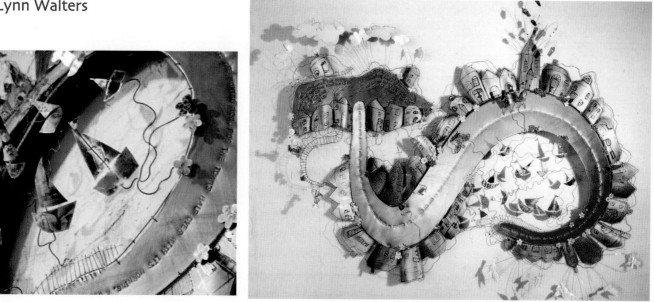

Craft in the Bay

Selwyn Gale

Selwyn designs and makes individual pieces of jewellery either to commission or for his permanent display at Craft in the Bay.

He works in the full range of precious metals often combined with precious and semi-precious stones and pearls.

Natural forms and textures, reflections and Celtic art all influence his jewellery designs.

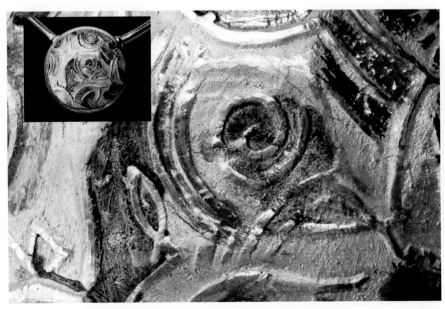

Sara Lloyd Morris

Sara's passion for making jewellery was launched with a demonstration of lost wax casting at school. Graduating from the School of Jewellery and Silversmithing, Birmingham. she moved to London to work for Andre Grima, Jermyn Street (who worked by appointment to HRH); Sara then started her own company and has been making jewellery ever since. Most of her inspiration comes from her travels and the Pembrokeshire coast.

Craft in the Bay

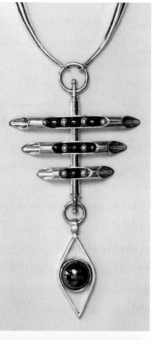

Clockwise from left:
Elizabeth Forrest – *mixed media*;
James Curley; Alison Moger – *mixed textiles*; Molly Curley;
Mandy Nash – *felt bangles*

Craft in the Bay

Galanthus Gallery & Cafe

P C ☕ 0% ♿

Wormbridge, Hereford HR2 9DH

Open 10am-5pm, six days a week including Sundays (closed Weds)

T: 01981 570506
E: info@galanthusgallery.com
www.galanthusgallery.com

Galanthus Gallery and Café is a contemporary art gallery and delightful café housed in a sympathetically converted 250-year-old barn in the heart of Herefordshire. The gallery shows a variety of high quality contemporary art, including painting, textiles, prints, photography, glass, ceramics and sculpture; and a changing selection of gorgeous, designer-made jewellery.

Our diverse exhibitions change six weekly; details are available from our website.

Galanthus Gallery and Café is open six days a week serving delicious lunches, homemade cakes and bread, ice cream and cheese from our dairy, 'illy' coffee, wine and beer in a relaxing atmosphere. In the summer, our sunny courtyard is the perfect place to linger over lunch.

The village of Wormbridge is eight miles from Hereford on the A465 Abergavenny road.

212   *Galanthus Gallery & Café*

Stephen Kingsford – page 263

The Hay Makers

St. John's Place, Hay-on-Wye
Hereford HR3 5BN
Open: daily 10.30am-1.30pm, 2pm-5pm, including Sunday

C 0%

T: 01497 820556
E: info@haymakers.co.uk
www.haymakers.co.uk

Situated in the world famous book town of Hay-on-Wye at the foot of the Black Mountains, The Hay Makers, a co-operative of professional designer makers, has flourished since opening in the 1980s. During this time the gallery has gained an enviable reputation for an exciting selection of high quality crafts at affordable prices and in a friendly atmosphere.

The gallery is always staffed by one of its members: Chris Armstrong – wood turning & furniture; Pat Birks – ceramics; Caitriona Cartwright – stone cutting & carving; Dawn Cripps – embroidery; Sue Forrest – painted silk ties; Harry Franklin – sculpture; Victoria Keeble – textiles; Chrissie Nash – silver jewellery and Nancy Sutcliffe – engraved glass.

In addition the gallery shows the work of some of the finest contemporary British craft makers in exhibitions throughout the year.

Clockwise from top left:
*Caitriona Cartwright – *stone-carving*, Sue Forrest – *ties* Dawn Cripps – *hearts* & Chrissie Nash – *silver*
*Nancy Sutcliffe – *engraved glass*
*Chrissie Nash & Dawn Cripps – *jewellery*
*Pat Birks – *ceramics*; *Chris Armstrong – *wood* & Harry Franklin – *sculpture*

Llantarnam Grange Arts Centre

St. David's Road
Cwmbran
Torfaen NP44 1PD

T: 01633 483321
E: llantarnamgrange@btconnect.com

Open: Monday-Saturday 10am-5pm (closed bank holidays)

P C ☕ ⊚

Llantarnam Grange Arts Centre is based in a large Victorian former family residence in the heart of Cwmbran. This historic building houses three temporary gallery spaces, presenting local, national and international contemporary craft and visual art. Our exhibitions change every eight weeks. Along side these exhibitions, we show a changing programme of craft and jewellery showcases high-lighting the talent of established and emerging makers. Our Craft Shop presents a range of work from makers in ceramic, jewellery, glass, wood and textiles from across Wales and beyond. There is also a Café Gallery displaying prints and serving food.

Directions

By Car: Follow Brown Tourist Signs showing the symbol of a pot. Free car parking in adjacent Glyndwr Car Park.

By Bus & Train: Stations within a few minutes walk.

Pedestrian: Signposted from Cwmbran Shopping Centre

Disabled Access:

Access to the Centre is via one step (portable wheel chair ramp available). Only the Ground Floor is Wheelchair accessible (Main Galleries, Craft Shop, Café, Adapted Toilet). The First Floor is via 14 stairs and is on three levels.

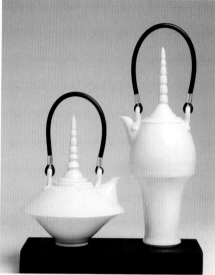

Clockwise from top left:
Virginia Graham;
Dean Button;
Melanie Brown;
Lisa Krigel – *ceramics;*
Sean Gordon

The Lion Gallery

15b Broad Street, Leominster
Herefordshire HR6 8BT
Open: Monday-Saturday 10am-5pm all year

T: 01568 611898
E: info@liongallery.com
www.liongallery.com

Situated in the ancient market town of Leominster, the Lion Gallery opened under it's present ownership in 2005.

It offers an extensive range of quality British art and craft. Studio and functional ceramicists such as Bridget Drakeford and Jennifer Hall are represented along with textile artists, printmakers, sculptors and glass-makers. Regular exhibitors include Sarah Roberts, Chris Noble, Rachel Ricketts and Stuart Ackroyd. A diverse range of contemporary jewellery is shown.

Fresh work is regularly introduced and featured artists are changed monthly. New makers are encouraged. An eclectic selection of unusual greetings cards are available, some of which are published in house.

Jon and Julie Harbottle

Jon and Julie Harbottle have been making pots for 29 years, after starting in Nottingham; they now live and work in South Shropshire. After many years of concentrating on their blue glaze, they felt a change was needed, so a new white has emerged. These pots, although similar in shape and form to the blue, are made using very smooth white clay and finished with a blend of different white glazes. The unglazed line around the middle has been replaced with an incised band to give some continuation of a theme.

Tanya Igic

Tanya Igic is a contemporary jeweller working with the finest quality, delicate leather in many beautiful shades and influenced by floral, natural or abstract motifs. Tanya produces a wide rage of necklaces, earrings, bracelets, corsages, chokers as well as bridal accessories. Her technique is unusual and innovative and involves a complex process. Silver wires and beads are then added as embellishments. Each piece is very labour intensive. This exciting and innovative work is available in more than 50 colours.

Penny Rees

Penny Rees studied fine art at Hereford College, having previously gained diplomas in specialist paint finishes and furniture design.

"Paint, especially oil paint, how it moves, what happens to it, the colour and smell, fill my working day. Each painting is a mix of stark line, vibrant colour and heavy impasto. Flowers, landscapes, boats have a tentative start, move through muddled times, before appearing at last as the work I wish it to be. My emotional response to the world around me is fairly obvious in my painterly works, these are ebullient in form and colour, endeavouring to encapsulate the surge of life."

Blake & Janette Mackinnon

"We produce a wide range of porcelain jewellery, including necklaces, earrings, brooches, bracelets, buttons and cuff links. The majority of the beads begin as extrusions, which are reworked by cutting, pressing and manipulation. Underglaze, glaze and lustre's in varied colours create an endless number of design combinations. We are experimenting with CNC to decorate our beads and slip cast clocks."
Left: *Porcelain cubes necklace & earrings, multicolour glaze decorated*

The Lion Gallery

Clockwise from top left:
Julia Linstead – *glass;*
Annie Hewett – *ceramics;*
Sarah Cheese – *embroidery;*
J & J Harbottle – *ceramics;*
Sarah Roberts – *textiles*

The Lion Gallery

Mikell Gallery

43 Lion Street, Hay on Wye
Hereford, HR3 5AA
Open: Daily 10am–5.30pm

♿

T: 01497 821806
E: mikellgallery@aol.com

Situated in this famous book town, Mikell Gallery has an enviable reputation for its collection of high quality art and modern craft. The owner, herself a stained glass artist, selects from the best local and British artists and designers, some established and some up and coming. Her emphasis is on glass and she seeks to provide an outstanding but affordable range of decorative and functional pieces. You will also find equally beautiful ceramics, jewellery, sculpture, prints and paintings.

Mikell Gallery

Clockwise from left:
Sam Hemmings – *jewellery;* Joanne Mitchell – *glass;*
Allister Malcolm – *glass;* Eryka Isaak – *glass;*
April Young – *smoke-fired ceramics*

Mikell Gallery

Old Chapel Gallery

P C 0% ☕

East Street, Pembridge, Nr Leominster
Herefordshire HR6 9HB
Open: Monday-Saturday 10am-5.30pm, Sunday 11am-5.30pm.

T: 01544 388842
E: yasminstrube@yahoo.com
www.oldchapelgallery.co.uk

Established in 1989 by Yasmin Strube, Old Chapel Gallery has become recognised as a centre of excellence for the arts, where work by both reputable local and nationally known artists and makers can be seen alongside innovative work by talented newcomers. The emphasis is on quality and originality, from glass, ceramics, jewellery, iron-work, sculpture, furniture, to textiles and knitwear and a diverse range of original watercolours, oils, pastels, etchings and aquatints. The gallery hosts regular and ever changing exhibitions and showcases. There is also an annual garden sculpture exhibition. A range of services are available through the gallery including commissioning and a "take it on appro" service for local and regular customers.

   The gallery has recently developed a new website for browsing and on-line shopping. The gallery is selected for quality by the Crafts Council and is a member of the ICGA. Friendly and knowledgeable staff are always on hand to welcome you and make your visit informative and memorable.

Jennie Gilbert

Jennie set up her first workshop in Surrey in 1993, she has since moved to Project Workshops in Hampshire. She produces an ever increasing range of tableware, with a selection of vases, pitchers, platters, lamp bases, bowls and bistro tables in the distinctive Mishima Range.

"Mishima is the inlaying of a contrasting slip into a pattern that has been impressed, stamped, or carved into the clay"

All Jennie's work is fired to 1280'c in a gas kiln and is suitable for everyday use. She sells her work at a few select Craft Fairs and Galleries and it is in private collections both in the U.K. and abroad.

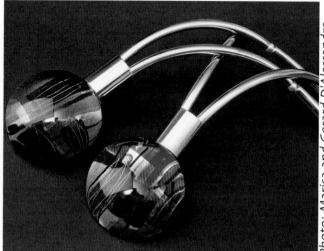

Photo: Marisa and Gerard D'Alessandro.

Gail Klevan

This innovative jewellery has evolved through continuous experimentation with modern acrylic materials. The pattern and drawing refract dense colour, with metallic gold and silver undertones across smooth and sculpted surfaces. These interact with the organic curvature and geometry of the highly polished optical quality acrylic shapes, creating shimmering, ever changing iridescence. Though bold, the jewellery is designed to adorn and flatter the wearer and is suitable with either casual or formal clothing and is comfortable and easy to wear for both everyday and special occasions. Like the Bakelite jewellery of the 1930's, these elegant and striking designs will become the classics of tomorrow.
Illustration:
Acrylic Dome chokers on white bronze tubes.

Helen Sinclair

Helen Sinclair trained at Wimbledon School of Art. She has been making sculpture for over 20 years and is still excited by the process.

The human figure is her primary subject, the actual figure (in movement and at rest, clothed and unclothed) and the figure as depicted by other artists in any medium and at any phase in history.

Most of Helen's work is cast in limited editions either in resin or bronze. With the help of a full-time technician, she makes her own moulds and does her own resin casting. She models the originals in plaster, wax, clay and mixed media and finds the materials that she works with can be as stimulating to her as the subject matter. She lives by the sea and collects driftwood, discarded plastic debris and other beach-found stuff, these introduce ever new and unexpected vocabulary into her work.

Helen lives in Wales with her husband, sculptor Terry Ryall.

From the left:
Fiona Morley – *wire on canvas;*
Deborah Scaldwell – *cold cast bronze sculptures;*
Carolyn Francis – *silver & resin jewellery*

Old Chapel Gallery

Opposite, clockwise from top left:
Michael Turner – *stainless steel;*
Paul Margetts – *forged iron;*
Rachel Ducker – *wire sculpture;*
Laurence McGowan – *stoneware;*
Frans Wesselman – *stained glass*

Old Chapel Gallery

Oriel-y-Felin Gallery

15 Ffordd-y-Felin, Trefin
Nr. St. David's, Pembrokeshire SA62 5AX
Open: Daily 11am-5pm Easter-end of October
Closed Mondays except Bank Holidays
Out of season please ring to check

T: 01348 837500
E: gallery@oriel-y-felin.com
www.oriel-y-felin.com

An exciting gallery in the delightful village of Trefin on the Pembrokeshire Coastal Path. Oriel-y-Felin has been described as a jewel in the artistic landscape.

Atmospheric works of this wonderful peninsula by St. David's artist Pauline Beynon, are shown with a constantly changing selection of carefully chosen paintings, ceramics, glass, bronzes, stainless steel works and jewellery.

Owner Angela Samuel and her business partner Pauline Beynon, have always strived to give their visitors a warm welcome so are thrilled to have been awarded the 2007 Les Routiers British Café of the Year Award. High standards in Food and Art!

Oriel-y-Felin Gallery

Clockwise from top left:
Susan Grindey & Pauline Beynon *both mixed media*; Phil Hayes – ceramics; Rob Whelpton – *raku*;
Michael Turner – *stainless steel*

Parkfields Gallery

4 High Street
Ross-on-Wye
Herefordshire HR9 5HL
Open: Monday-Saturday 9.30am-5pmk

C 0% &

T: 01989 565266
E: info@parkfieldsgallery.co.uk
www.parkfieldsgallery.co.uk

Set in the picturesque town of Ross-on-Wye, Parkfields Gallery exhibits a diverse and extensive range of the highest quality art and contemporary craft. Work by established local artists and craftspeople, together with the very best from across the UK is displayed.

2007 marks our 10th year in business and we continue to find fresh, new talent to exhibit alongside established makers. Work ranges from paintings, prints, pottery, glassware and sculpture to stunning jewellery, designer textiles and superb handmade furniture.

The changing exhibition programme, with a new, themed, multi-media exhibition each month, ensures there is always something different to view. With a welcoming, friendly atmosphere, visitors are encouraged to browse and enjoy the diversity of work

on display.
Parkfields Gallery is happy to organise special commissions from the makers and operates an interest free Art Buyers Credit Scheme. Join Parkfields

Gallery mailing list and you will receive their quarterly newsletter, keeping you informed about forthcoming exhibitions and events.

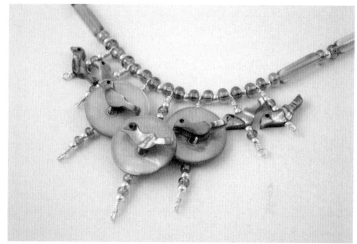

Clockwise from top left:
Adrienne Craddock – *prints*; Sara Withers;
Walter Keeler; Colin Chetwood – *Light/metal*;
Tamsin Abbott – *glass*

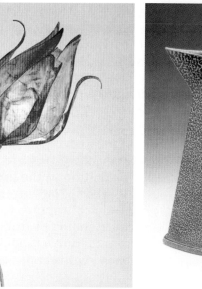

The Potters' Gallery

♿

1 High Street, Conwy
North Wales LL32 8DB

T: 01492 593590
E: seking@postmaster.co.uk

Open: Daily 10am-5pm (October-March closed on Wednesdays)

Situated in the medieval town of Conwy, The Potters' Gallery, Oriel y Crochenwyr, exhibits a wide range of ceramic works. On display is the work of the members of the North Wales Potters, a co-operative of 20 selected regional artists who run the gallery as a collective project, to enhance the art scene of North Wales.

The gallery's standards of excellence, both technical and aesthetic, give visitors a great choice of high quality ceramics. The items range from everyday domestic ware, with an individual touch, to exclusive limited production pieces for collectors. They are presented by the artists themselves in the inviting and friendly atmosphere of the gallery.

In addition to the promotion of local art, The Potters' Gallery actively contributes to an understanding of studio ceramics for everybody by offering workshops. It also runs exhibitions at other venues.

Above: Bev Bel Hughes
Top Right: Willie Carter
Right: Sonja Moss-Dolega

The Potter's Gallery

Craig Carsley – pages 126 & 7

Twenty Twenty

0%

3/4 High Street
Much Wenlock
Shropshire TF13 6AA
Open: Tuesday-Saturday 10am-5.30pm

T: 01952 727952
E: info@twenty-twenty.co.uk
www.twenty-twenty.co.uk

Situated in a prominent position on the High Street in the delightful town of Much Wenlock, Twenty Twenty is a contemporary craft and art gallery and shop with an excellent reputation.

The gallery has recently expanded to create more exhibition space and has 4 double windows for additional display areas to highlight the work of individual artists and makers.

Monthly exhibitions are held at Twenty Twenty as well as the gallery exhibiting in London at shows such as 20/21 International Art Fair at the RCA and The Affordable Art Fair in Battersea.

Twenty Twenty also offers 'Own Art' the Arts Council supported loan scheme which makes purchasing art affordable.

Twenty Twenty

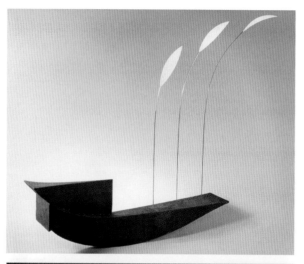

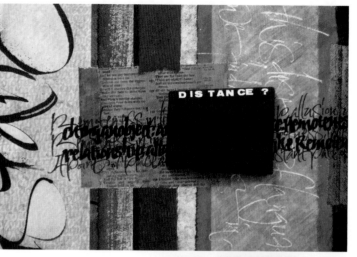

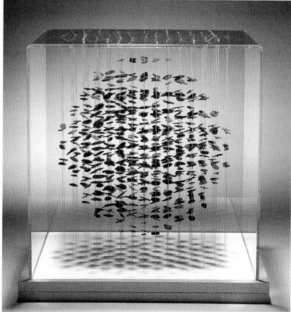

Clockwise from
top left:
Matthew Tomalin –
cast iron sculpture;
Mick Paine – *text
based artwork;*
Pamela Rawnsley –
silver vessels;
Dail Behennah –
*pebble sphere, natural
sculpture*

Victoria Fearn Gallery

P C ♿

6B Heol y Deri, Rhiwbina
Cardiff CF14 6HF
Open: Monday-Saturday 9.30am-5.30pm

T: 029 2052 0884
E: victoriafearngallery@hotmail.com
www.victoriafearngallery.co.uk

The gallery is situated in the busy village of Rhiwbina, on the outskirts of Cardiff, with easy access from the M4 and space for parking outside the building.

Mother and daughter, Carole and Victoria Fearn opened the gallery in 2004 and specialise in contemporary British crafts. They are delighted to show an excellent collection of work by well established local and nationally known designers and craftspeople.

There is always a large selection of glass, ceramics, sculpture, jewellery, paintings, wood and textiles to choose from. Victoria's own workshop is on the premises where she designs and makes a wide range of silverware and jewellery, which is also on display. With the expansion of the gallery in 2005, the second larger room allows bi-monthly,

changing exhibitions and is an area for larger works of art, sculpture and paintings.

The gallery is already gaining a reputation for having an exciting range of work that is constantly changing. There are monthly spotlights on ceramics and jewellery in the main gallery which allows an opportunity to feature a more extensive group of work by one or two selected makers.

With a welcoming friendly atmosphere, Carole and Victoria encourage visitors to browse and enjoy the diversity of work on display. They are always on the look out for new and exciting designers to display their work in the gallery.

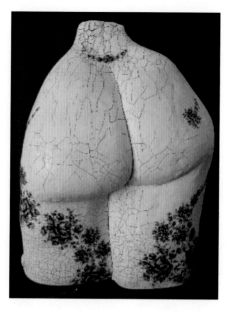

Sonje Hibbert

Sonje Hibbert is a ceramic artist whose work fuses a fascination of eastern cultures and the traditional W.European styles.

The sensual figurative sculptures, whilst being tactile and often humorous, on a more serious note attempt to portray the clichés that surround the western perceptions of the female form. The large decorative jugs are made from a grogged stoneware, with the use of plaster moulds and hand building techniques.

Anne Bosset

Anne Bosset was born in Kenya, and spent much of her childhood in Japan and New Zealand. All three of these countries later became aspects of her painting, in particular the luminosity of Africa's open skies and the vast tracts of land.

In 1979 her family moved to Llangynidr, a village near Crickhowell, with stunning views of the Black Mountains and the river Usk. The variations in the light and landscape of this area have inspired much of her recent work .

She paints principally in water colour and acrylic, using layers of transparent paint and hand-made paper to create depth in her work. She has a gallery and studio in the Charente Maritime in France.

Clockwise from top left:
Magical Woods – *Ht 13"*;
Victoria Fearn – *silversmith*;
Gwen Davis – *bead jewellery*;
Julie Pettitt – *porcelain*;
Louis Thompson – *glass*

Chris Poole – photography – page 163

Wobage Makers Gallery

P C ☕ ♿

Wobage Farm, Upton Bishop
Herefordshire HR9 7QP
Open: Thursday-Sunday 10am-5pm and by appointment
Closed January-February

T: 01989 780495
E: ben.casson@virgin.net
www.wobagecrafts.co.uk

In 1977 Michael and Sheila Casson moved to Wobage Farm which lies on the B4224 Hereford road out of Upton Bishop - see map above.

The late 18th century sandstone farm buildings have been converted into craft studios for eight craftspeople. Each working individually and sharing the facilities.

There are four potters: Sheila Casson, Patia Davis, Petra Reynolds and Jeremy Steward. Clair Hodgson is a jeweller and her sister Lynn Hodgson a wood carver and furniture maker, while Ben Casson also designs and makes furniture.

All the work in the showroom is made on the premises with the exception of pots from France made by Andrew and Clare McGarva, who worked here for ten years. The makers supply a wide range of items in size and price.

240

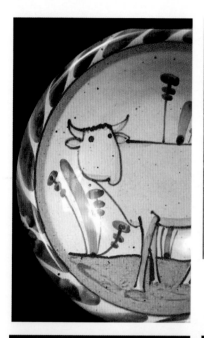
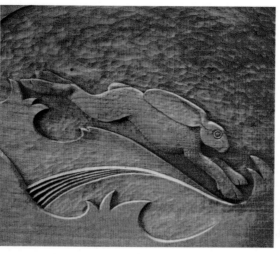

Clockwise from top left:
Andrew & Clare McGarva; Lynn Hodgson –
wood carving; Clair Hodgson – *jewellery*;
Sheila Casson *also far left;* Jeremy Steward

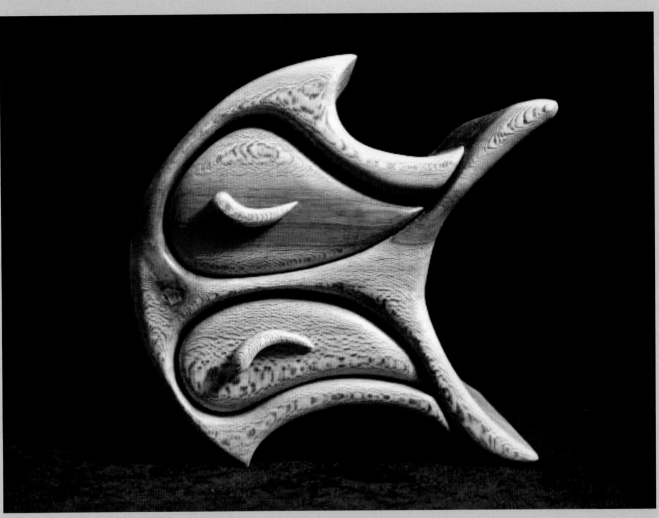

Peter Vernon – page 73

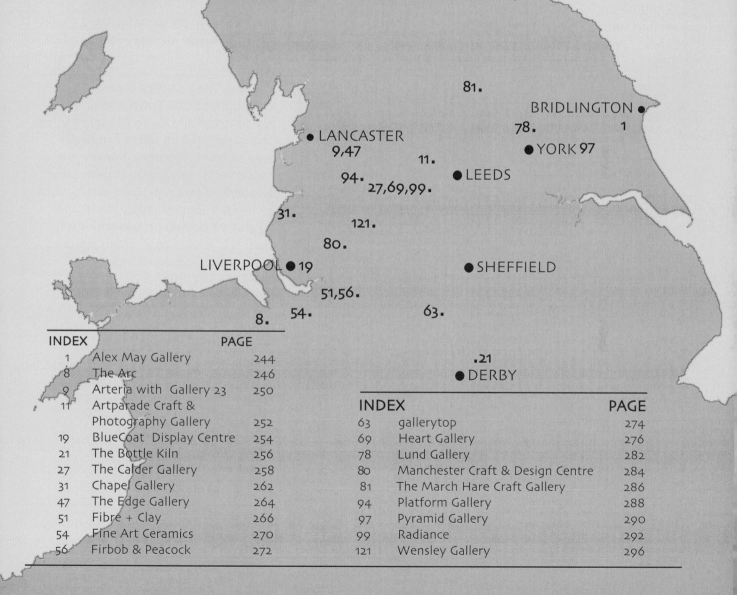

Northern England

81.

BRIDLINGTON

●LANCASTER
9,47

78.

1

●YORK 97

11.

94.

●LEEDS

27,69,99.

31.

121.

80.

LIVERPOOL●19

●SHEFFIELD

51,56.

54.

63.

8.

.21

●DERBY

Alex May Gallery

P C

15 High Street, Old Town
Bridlington, Yorkshire YO16 4PR
Open: Tuesday-Saturday 10am-4pm,
Sunday and Monday appointments only

T: 01262 409773
E: info@alexmaygallery.co.uk
www.alexmaygallery.co.uk

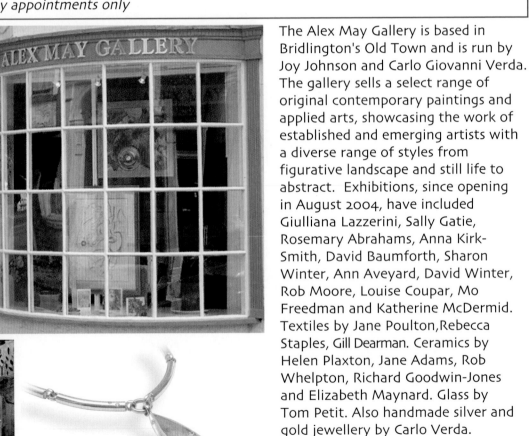

The Alex May Gallery is based in Bridlington's Old Town and is run by Joy Johnson and Carlo Giovanni Verda. The gallery sells a select range of original contemporary paintings and applied arts, showcasing the work of established and emerging artists with a diverse range of styles from figurative landscape and still life to abstract. Exhibitions, since opening in August 2004, have included Giulliana Lazzerini, Sally Gatie, Rosemary Abrahams, Anna Kirk-Smith, David Baumforth, Sharon Winter, Ann Aveyard, David Winter, Rob Moore, Louise Coupar, Mo Freedman and Katherine McDermid. Textiles by Jane Poulton, Rebecca Staples, Gill Dearman. Ceramics by Helen Plaxton, Jane Adams, Rob Whelpton, Richard Goodwin-Jones and Elizabeth Maynard. Glass by Tom Petit. Also handmade silver and gold jewellery by Carlo Verda.

Sharon Winter – *Venus, oil painting*
Carlo Verda – *jewellery*

Alex May Gallery

Tina Vlassopulos – porcelain – page 95

The Arc

P

4 Commonhall Street, off Bridge Street
Chester CH1 2BJ
Open: Tuesday-Saturday 10am-5pm

T: 01244 348379
E: enquiries@thearcgallery.co.uk
www.thearcgallery.co.uk

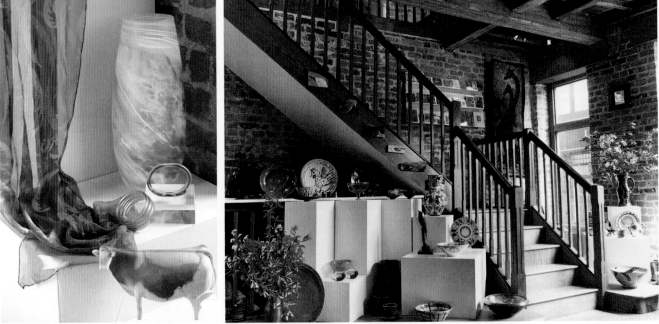

The Arc contemporary craft gallery is housed in an 18th century brick and timber warehouse. Our building is greatly admired by many visitors and also creates a beautiful backdrop for the varied contemporary work we show, by designers and makers from all corners of the British Isles. With special emphasis on ceramics and textiles, jewellery and leather, The Arc is also a rewarding hunting ground for the unusual gift or special present.

   Selection of work is based upon craftsmanship, and the skills that reveal the qualities of the chosen material, light through glass, glaze on clay, the grain and weight of wood, the curve of acrylic or spun pewter. Jewellery is selected for wit and wearability, fashion and interior textiles for the glorious richness of colour and imagination.

The Arc

Lesley Strickland

My interest in making jewellery began in 1976 when I attended evening classes at the City Literary Institute in London. I was extremely fortunate to have an excellent and inspiring teacher, Jennifer Pike. After three years, I worked part-time as a secretary while I set up my business.

I have continued to develop a strong personal style over the years, firstly in acrylic and now cellulose acetate. I enjoy working in the latter, as I can create more fluid and organic forms.

I use basic jewellery techniques with heat forming. The final finish is vitally important as I want the wearer to have a very tactile relationship with each piece. I aim to create simple elegant work which can be seen in galleries across the UK and abroad.

Amanda Woakes

Amanda Woakes designs stunning necklaces, bracelets and earrings using a combination of glass beads, antique and found buttons on sterling silver and suede. Her eclectic use of tonal and vibrant colour palettes creates jewellery that spans a wide range of tastes and occasions. Each piece is individually designed. Commissions can also be made to complement specific outfits and seasonal fashions.

Margo Selby

Margo Selby is an award-winning British textile designer with a bold approach to creating high-quality woven fabric. Her work is recognisable for its three-dimensional structure, striking colour and geometric pattern.

The Silk Bubble Collection employs her trademark fabrics for cushions, scarves, ties, bow-ties and gifts. All are available in sumptuous colour and texture combinations.

Margo Selby develops her fabrics on a hand-loom in a London studio; they are then woven to her requirements by silk mills in the UK. She also offers a bespoke service for individual textile artworks, bedspreads and themed cushion collections in luxury fibres.

Andrew Hazelden

Trained at Epsom Art School 1981 to 1984. After leaving Epsom Andrew joined the team of potters at Aldermaston. There he learnt the technique of tin-glazed earthenware, making and painting Aldermaston shapes up to closure of the pottery in 1993. Since then Andrew has worked independently at Aldermaston until January 2007. He has now established a pottery at Yarnton in Oxfordshire and produces domestic ware and commemorative orders.

The Arc

From top left clockwise:
Bruno Charron – *wood*;
Delyth Jones – *ceramics*;
E & M – *studio glass*; Mirka Golden-
Hann – *saltglaze stoneware*;
Monica Boxley – *leather*

Arteria with Gallery 23

P C

23 Brock Street
Lancaster LA1 1UR
Open: Monday-Saturday 10am-5pm

T: 01524 61111
E: arteriagallery23@aol.com
www.arteriawithgallery23.co.uk

Arteria with Gallery 23 is housed in a recently renovated late 1800's building, conveniently situated in the city centre of historic Lancaster. Distinctively integrated over two spacious floors; the ground floor shop offers an exceptional range of innovative, design-led gifts and interior arts. The products are carefully selected from the very best suppliers worldwide to provide customers with an exclusive, affordable lifestyle collection.

Located on the first floor Gallery 23 offers a visually refreshing collection of fine art and contemporary crafts, with a strong focus on quality and originality of design. A changing exhibition programme throughout the year spotlights the work of local and national contemporary artists and designers.

Offering a relaxed and friendly environment you will find new stylish accessories for the home or the perfect gift for that special occasion. For simply enjoying art and design come and see our complete lifestyle collection for a shopping experience with a personal touch.

Rachel Hearne

Memories and impressions of my surroundings are the biggest source of inspiration while designing jewellery. Items such as rocks, bark, seeds, petals and pollen have become recurrent themes found in my collections.

With my chosen techniques and materials, I am able to achieve a delicate play between texture, line and form giving my work a modern yet classic look that can be worn during any occasion.

The jewellery is produced at my studio in Lancaster and designs are handcrafted out of sterling silver, accompanied by individually selected semi-precious stones and freshwater pearls, to create a contemporary piece as individual as the wearer.

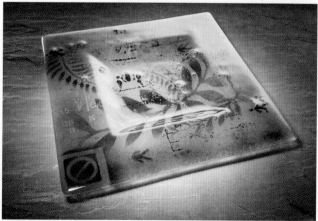

From top right:
Vicki Mulligan – *jewellery*
Timea Sido – *ceramics*
& Stephanie Bowen – *glass*

ArtParade
Craft & Photography Gallery

P C 0% ♿

1 Victoria Road
Saltaire BD18 3LA
Open: Tuesday to Sunday 10am-6pm. Closed Mondays except Bank Holidays

T: 01274 590619
E: info@artparade.co.uk
www.artparade.co.uk

This beautiful spacious gallery, in the World Heritage Site village of Saltaire, is special in offering both contemporary designer crafts and original fine art photography. ArtParade originated as PhotoFolio, the photography gallery in Salts Mill, but has now relocated across the road.

"The new gallery lends itself beautifully to displaying crafts on the ground floor, where the light floods in, and photography on the lower ground floor, where we have two rooms and lots of wall space" said owner Beverley Stewart. "The spiral staircase between the two adds masses of character, but we also have disabled access for those who need it."

"It's a lovely environment to work in, and amongst so many beautiful things. I only hope to be able to offer my customers an equally delightful experience. Our twin aims are to offer the highest quality work and have the friendliest gallery you could ever wish to return to."
Extract from newspaper report on opening December 2005

Regularly changing exhibitions featuring the new work of leading and emerging British designers, makers and photographers are detailed on our web site.

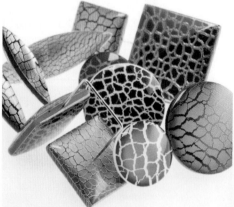

Clockwise from top left:
Wendy-Sarah Pacey – *acrylic & silver jewellery;* Terry Cryer – *photography;* Dominic Fondé – *blown glass etched with his own Haiku;* Antonia Salmon – *ceramics;* John Angerson – *photography*

Bluecoat Display Centre

P C ☕ 0% ♿

Bluecoat Chambers
College Lane, Liverpool L1 3BZ
Open: Monday-Saturday 10am-5.30pm

T: 0151 709 4014
E: crafts@bluecoatdisplaycentre.com
www.bluecoatdisplaycentre.com

The Bluecoat Display Centre is a haven for buyers of everything exquisite in the field of contemporary craft and design, situated in the Bluecoat, a thriving contemporary arts centre in a newly refurbished Queen Anne building, located in the heart of Liverpool. The city is the European Capital of Culture in 2008 and the Display Centre will contribute with its own ambitious programme of group and solo exhibitions, workshops and lectures.

The Bluecoat Display Centre originated as one of this country's earliest craft galleries in 1959, founded by Robert Gardner-Medwin, Professor of Architecture at Liverpool University. We celebrate the Display Centre's 50th Anniversary year in 2009 with an exciting programme of exhibitions and events. Gardner-Medwin intended the work shown at the Display Centre to enhance good architecture and interior design and today we find we are still the place that attracts national and international collectors as well as leading professionals involved in Liverpool's renaissance.

The Bluecoat Display Centre promotes nationally and also internationally, through exhibition, display and sales, emphasising excellence in design and work-manship in contemporary applied art, and increasing public awareness and appreciation of the work of leading and emerging artists.

Our aims and intentions are to support individual makers within the creative industries by selling and showing their work in a stimulating, educating and sympathetic environment.

254

Bluecoat Display Centre

Rebecca Gouldson

A recipient of numerous awards and residencies, Rebecca has been producing metalwork since 2001 and began making her wall mounted pieces in 2004. From her Liverpool studio, Rebecca Gouldson produces intricately textured and beautifully constructed metal forms and wall pieces, using soldering, etching, electroplating and patination. Imagery from both the built and the natural environment influence the marks, patterns and textures she applies to metal, drawing and making prints from studies of buildings, from varying viewpoints. Rebecca also cites the paintings of Antoni Tapies and Ben Nicholson, and the jeweller Manfred Bishcoff as influences on her work. Rebecca studied for a BA (hons) degree in woods, metals and plastics at the University of Wolverhampton, graduating in 2002. She was selected for the Crafts Council's Next Move scheme as artist in residence at Liverpool Hope University for 2003-04.

Miranda Sharpe

Miranda Sharpe started her business designing and making contemporary jewellery in 2001, she has exhibited and sold her work widely across the UK and ventured into the international market place. By combining use of both precious and non-precious materials Miranda produces innovative jewellery that explores the notion of beauty, her approach to jewellery is to express what interests her visually, such as aspects of nature, in an abstracted way to create designs that vary from easily wearable pieces to more dramatic pieces. " I am interested in exploiting the qualities of resin, creating precious items from a material normally perceived as functional, I am continually evolving my work and developing new designs". Each piece of jewellery is mainly made and finished by hand, for which a variety of hand processes are employed, with recent addition of some cast elements.

The Bottle Kiln

P ☕ ♿

High Lane, West Hallam
Near Ilkeston
Derbyshire DE7 6HP
Open: Tuesday-Sunday from 10am-5pm closed Bank Holidays

T: 0115 932 9442
E: info@bottlekiln.co.uk
www.bottlekiln.co.uk

"An oasis of calm and a rich source of inspiration, the Bottle Kiln provides both a welcome rest from the buzzing modern world and a tempting and varied collection of visual delights.

Built on the site of a former pottery containing an unusual old bottle-necked kiln, it comprises areas for contemporary craft - housed in and around the kiln itself - fine art, giftware, cards, jewellery and homewares, as well as an award-winning cafe selling teas, coffees and lunches. Outside a tranquil garden based on the theme of a japanese tea garden provides an area to take refreshments in good weather.

In the crafts displays we show a range of ceramics and glass by regional and national makers, and have a particular interest in hand-made contemporary jewellery, with the overall aim of extending a broad appeal both to experienced gallery-goers and total newcomers, whilst maintaining a high standard throughout.

Over 20 years old and now firmly established as a key arts venue in its area, the Bottle Kiln has become extremely popular both to visitors from the region and further afield, attracting all those who seek objects that are well-chosen, beautiful and unusual."

The Bottle Kiln

Clockwise from top left:

Abbott & Ellwood – *metal sculpture*; Rachel Barker;
Sarah Vernon – *ceramics*; Will Shakspeare – *glass*; Jennifer Hall

The Calder Gallery

C 0% ♿

20 Market Street
Hebden Bridge
West Yorkshire HX7 6AA
Open: Wednesday-Saturday 10am-5.30pm, Sunday 11am-5pm

T: 01422 843832
E: sue@caldergallery.co.uk
www.caldergallery.co.uk

The Calder Gallery is situated in Hebden Bridge in the heart of the Pennines. It is a town of tremendous character and a very popular centre for visitors to West Yorkshire as there is a range of artistic, musical and cultural activities happening throughout the year, including the very popular Arts Festival in early Summer. As a result there are a wide variety of cafés, bars and inns that cater for all tastes.

The Calder Gallery opened its doors in April 2005 and has established a reputation for high quality original works of art. Owned and run by Sue Allinson and Phil Withersby, the Gallery hosts a regularly changing mixed exhibition in the lower room and a monthly solo exhibition in the upper room for most of the year.

Sue and Phil revel in finding work which is original and

different. Since opening they have gained a reputation for eye-catching, witty sculptural pieces that they delight in placing in the window.

Sue and Phil's infectious enthusiasm and knowledgeable approach ensure that your visit will be a pleasant experience. Details of exhibitions and opening times can be found on the website.

Phil Withersby – Calder Gallery's Resident Artist

Etchings and paintings in oils and watercolours – images of Northern landscape – clockwise from top left: Evening Sky nr Peckett Well 1640 x 1070 cms; Rocks nr Colden; Wet Field, Halsall Moss 22 x 16cms; The Big Tree 16 x 10cms & Silverdale Beach II, 90 x 75cms

The Calder Gallery

Kate Lycett

After studying textiles at university and working for several years as a commercial textile designer Kate decided to escape and have some fun. The influence of surface pattern and a love of colour and decoration is ever present in her unusual interpretations of the local landscape.

"I love the work of artists that incorporate flat pattern into their work – people like Schiele, Hundertwasser and Klimt who reduced land-scapes down to flat planes. I love to exaggerate the lines and shapes present in the environment, and bring out the decorative elements like plant pots and lines of washing that make a place look loved and lived in."

As well as originals Kate produces Gicleé prints of her work. These are each hand-finished with machine embroidery and gold leaf making each piece quite different.

Duncan Thurlby

Since leaving Loughborough College of Art & Design in 1990, Duncan has been working full time as a metal sculptor.

Initially concentrating on commission work for music and entertainment venues, including Chelsea Football Club, Camden Palace and Chicago Rock Café to name but a few, Duncan has more recently focussed his attention on gallery pieces and commissions for private clients as far afield as America and Australia.

His work ranges from his ever popular hounds through pelicans, giant conker shells, toucans and alligators to large scale architectural water sculptures. His inspiration is plucked from the natural world, never too literally or seriously, a sense of character and humour being essential in all of his creations. Using a range of hand working techniques the final pieces emerge as a result of this rather unnatural evolution.

Kate Boyce

Kate Boyce has achieved recognition for her vibrant landscapes and narrative studies. Her individual style combines painterly and graphic effect. Acrylic paint and photographic collage work in harmony on canvas. Atmosphere and light are captured in wonderful reflective colour. Kate's paintings are in private and corporate collections throughout the UK. She lives and works in Hebden Bridge.

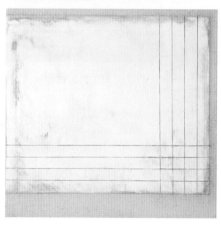

From the left:
Susan Laughton – 'Free' *mixed Media 30 x 30cms*;
Gilda Dickinson – 'Moorland Landscape' *30 x 30cms*;
Patricia McAllister – *aluminium resin Ht 70cms*

Chapel Gallery

St. Helens Road, Ormskirk
Lancashire L39 4QR
Open: Tuesday-Saturday 10am-4.30pm

🍵 0% ♿

T: 01695 571328
E: chapel.gallery@westlancsdc.gov.uk
www.chapelgallery.org.uk

Chapel Gallery is located in the medieval market town of Ormskirk and has developed an excellent reputation regionally. Its innovative exhibition programme, incorporating educational activities for all, with the high-quality gift items in the Contemporary Craft Shop and the delicious Café menu, make any visit a pleasure.

The Chapel Gallery team curates and installs a diverse programme of exhibitions and showcases. These programmes also feature the work of prominent artists such as David Hockney, organised through the Hayward Gallery Touring Exhibitions and Julie Arkell, through the Ruthin Craft Centre.

Located within the Gallery is a contemporary craft shop that is a shopper's paradise. It offers a wide range of luxury items including hand crafted textiles, glassware, jewellery, metal work and ceramics and these items are available for purchase through the Arts Council England's Own Art scheme. The Gallery Café is also well worth a visit, its welcoming atmosphere and menu of light lunches, speciality coffees and luxury cakes, is always a treat.

There are a variety of other events and services including an engaging education programme for schools and colleges, a well established Art Club facilitated by professional artists and a successful holiday activities programme featuring both visual and performance art workshops. Programmes also feature the annual West Lancashire Open Exhibition, the Youth Open Exhibition, our Christmas Fine Art and Contemporary Craft Event and a variety of artists talks and family friendly activities.

The Gallery is situated in the town centre approximately 100 yards from Ormskirk Bus Station, a town centre car park and is approximately a five minute walk from Ormskirk Railway Station.

Stephen Kingsford

I have always had a keen interest in the country-side, and this has been reflected in my work. I find that it produces many of the starting points for new designs and decorations. More recently my interest in music has provided a new focus for both my Raku and smoke fired pieces. In the smoke firing process I prefer to use oak as it gives a range of colours from blue-greys to intense blacks which enhance the sculptural elements in my work. I mix all my own glazes, and prefer to use translucent colours which give a greater depth and almost a jewel-like quality to the work.

Emma Lagardere

The inspiration for my jewellery is derived from my interest in the unseen world; objects which can only be observed through a microscope or telescope, but never with the naked eye.

Even though we accept these entities exist, they are essentially intangible and so can be accessed as things of beauty rather than seen as deadly killer viruses or monstrous stars of huge power.

It is in the spirit of this separation that I use silver and polyester resin as the principal materials for these pieces.

The Edge Gallery

P C 0% ♿

20-22 King Street, Lancaster
Lancashire LA1 1JY
Open: Tuesday-Saturday 10am-5pm

T: 01524 66029
E: ian@theedgegallery.co.uk
www.theedgegallery.co.uk

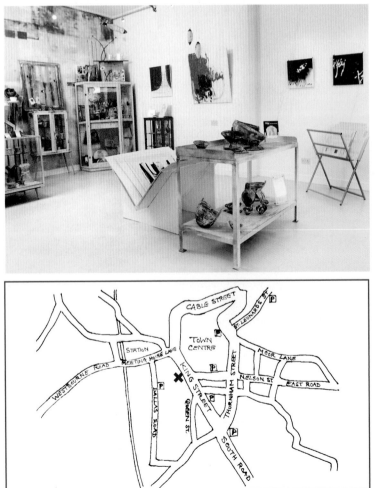

The Edge Gallery was established in 2003 by Ian and Priscilla Jones and is situated in the heart of Lancaster's historic city centre. Conveniently located for visitors arriving by road or public transport, and is just fifteen minuets drive from the coast with scenic views across Morecambe Bay.

The gallery has a strong reputation for exhibiting an exciting programme of contemporary fine and applied art and is committed to promoting the work of artists from across the U.K. and Europe. Our wide selection includes jewellery, ceramics, textiles, sculpture, paintings, prints, accessories and handmade greeting cards. The gallery has a small sculpture garden at the rear of the gallery that has enabled us to extend our range of exhibits to house outdoor work suitable for gardens and patios.

The gallery also runs a regular educational programme of artist led workshops.

We offer a commissioning service, gift vouchers and 0% finance.

Priscilla Jones

Priscilla has been producing contemporary stitched mixed media pieces in 2D and 3D since completing her degree in embroidery at in 1997. Priscilla draws her inspiration from a variety of sources exploring the concept of identity, memory and nostalgia. These themes underpin a range of areas within her work including free-lance designs for fashion and interior fabrics, wall paper and greeting cards exporting to Europe, Australia and the U.S.A.

Continuously exhibiting across the U.K. Priscilla supplies many galleries and retail outlets with collections of her quirky teacups, teapots and cakes created from found vintage materials and haberdashery. Priscilla also lectures part-time in Higher Education and runs a variety of independent workshops. In 2006 Priscilla won the prestigious 'Best Product' award at Flair.

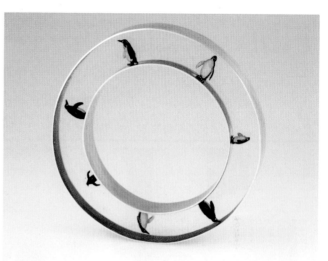

Helen Noakes

A series of evening workshops, a part-time three year London Open College Network course and an award (Best use of Metalwork and Techniques Victoria & Albert Museum's 'Inspired by....' Competition, 1999), lured jewellery designer-maker Helen Noakes from corporate London to a Wiltshire jewellery work-bench in late 2004. Helen's jewellery is spiked with humour and tiny surprises. Using miniature models as the nucleus of her designs the small figures are cast in resin and set in simple, finely handcrafted silver settings. The hard-to-find figures that have become the focus of her collection run the gamut from penguins, scuba divers and terriers to cheeky punk rockers. Other clever designs feature Belle Epoque swimmers gliding around a resin and silver cuff, and sheep grazing at the bottom of a pendant charm.

Fibre + Clay

34a King Street, Knutsford,
Cheshire, WA16 6DW
Open: Tuesday, Wednesday and Friday 11am-5pm,
Thursday 11am-7pm (Knit gatherings 7pm-10pm) Saturday 10am-5pm

T: 01565 652035
E: fibreandclay@aol.com
www.fibreandclay.co.uk

Fibre + Clay is an exciting new gallery that combines its owners' twin passions for contemporary ceramics and textile art. In a listed building in the elegant market town of Knutsford, the light and airy ground floor space showcases work by leading British ceramicists and textile artists, emerging designer-makers as well as by internationally renowned craftspeople based in the owners' previous home, South Africa.

Each piece is carefully selected for the originality of its design and high quality of craftsmanship, and sourced directly from the maker's studio. The ever changing collection is a true celebration of texture, colour, shape and form, and a treasure trove for the serious collector or anyone looking for unusual gifts, wearable art and both functional and decorative homeware pieces.

In addition to the gallery space, you will find a knit studio on the first floor selling a whole range of exquisite luxury yarns for hand knitting and crochet. Regular workshops and informal weekly knit gatherings are held for those interested in learning a new skill or brushing up on a much loved hobby.

Clockwise from top left:
Hennie Meyer;
Ralph Johnson;
Francoise Dufuyard;
David Alnatt; Anna Silverton

Fibre + Clay

267

Clockwise from top left:
Forward Bears;
Tait & Style and Vicky B Bags;
Lynsey Walters – *felt*; Liz Clay;
Mielie; Ronel Jordaan

LoCo Glass – pages 169 & 174

Fine Art Ceramics

P C

The Coach House, Daleford Manor
Dalefords Lane, Sandiway, Northwich, Cheshire CW8 2BT
Open: Thursday-Sunday 11am-5pm or by appointment
Check for seasonal variations.

T: 01606 883391
E: plantpotts@btinternet.com

Anne and Philip Plant would like to invite all who are interested in ceramics to their working studio and the recently created gallery. The gallery is situated in the 19th century Daleford Manor stable block, which is hidden down a rural farm lane.

Over a period of 35 years the old horse loose-boxes have been converted into a working studio; more recently the hay loft has been transformed to provide 70 square metres of gallery space. This has provided the opportunity for Anne and Philip to display their unusual ceramic wall hangings, and many maquettes from various large scale commissioned ceramic murals.

As the walls are mainly used to display their own work, the owners have space to show work from other ceramic artists in the rest of the gallery. They buy selected pieces from: Peter Beard, Peter Ilsley, Elaine Peto, Tony Laverick, Eddie and Margaret Curtis, Willy V. Bussel (Holland), Valerie Shelton, Caroline Whyman, Jane Perryman, Alain de Jardin (France) and other ceramic artists whose work they like.

Top right: Christy Keeney – *ceramics ht 13/15"*
Bottom left: Peter Beard – *sandblasted porcelain Ht 10"*
All others: Anne Plant – *ceramic plaques from 13"x7" – 13"x25"*

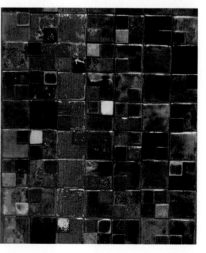

Fine Art Ceramics

Firbob & Peacock

P C ☕ 0%

76, King Street
Knutsford
Cheshire WA16 6ED
Open: Tuesday-Saturday 11am-5pm; Sunday noon-4pm

T: 01565 621156
E: firbob76@yahoo.co.uk
www.firbobandpeacock.co.uk

Firbob & Peacock is a dynamic, contemporary art and craft gallery located close to Tatton Park in the centre of the beautiful, bustling market town of Knutsford.

The gallery's three rooms house an ever-changing collection of selected art pieces. An exciting range of original work is featured including painting, ceramics, jewellery, furniture and sculpture from some of the UK's leading artists and craftspeople as well as emerging talent.

Above the gallery is Canvas Lounge – a licensed entrée bar serving tasty bites and drinks. This additional level extends outside to a roof terrace and sculpture garden. The informal atmosphere allows visitors to enjoy the art at leisure before

relaxing with a coffee and some food.

A range of services is available through the gallery including commissioning, corporate art and a try-before-you-buy service for local clients.

Photo: Alice Creed

Clockwise from top left: Lewis Noble – *watercolour on gesso panel 20 x 40cms*; Linda Calvert Ht 7cms & Janet Creed *both slipcast earthenware*; Simon Shaw – *ceramic & glass* Ht 12"; Kokkino – *jewellery*

gallerytop

P C 0% ♿

Chatsworth Road
Rowsley, Matlock
Derbyshire DE4 2EH
Open: Wednesday-Sunday 10am-5pm

T: 01629 735580
E:info@gallerytop.co.uk
www.gallerytop.co.uk

Set among the rolling hills of North Derbyshire, the small village of Rowsley is situated on the edges of the Peak District National Park and the Duke of Devonshire's rural estate with it's magnificent Chatsworth House. The village is near Elizabethan Haddon Hall and the thriving market town of Bakewell.

gallerytop was established in 2004 and the aim of the gallery is to offer a diverse range of contemporary fine and applied art by both established and emerging artists. The team has a wealth of experience in the arts and seeks to present the very highest quality work by UK artists in a way which is informative and enjoyable.

The gallery curates a programme of innovative exhibitions celebrating the richness and diversity of contemporary art, including painting, sculpture, ceramics, glass and jewellery.

Clockwise from top left:
Rebecca Gouldson – *metal*
Anna Noel – *ceramics*
Charlie Macpherson – *glass*
Eddie Curtis – *ceramics*;
Alison Macleod – *jewellery*

gallerytop

Heart Gallery

P C ♿

The Arts Centre, 4a Market Street
Hebden Bridge, West Yorkshire HX7 6AA
*Open: Wednesday–Friday 10.30am-5.00pm, Saturday 10.30am-5.30pm,
Sunday noon-4pm, closed Monday-Tuesday*

T: 01422 845845
E: alison@heartgallery.co.uk
www.heartgallery.co.uk

Heart Gallery is owned and run by Alison Bartram who has sympathetically designed its interesting layout, achieving an inviting and serene space that not only compliments the architecture of the building, a former Chapel, but also provides the perfect space to exhibit fresh, innovative and exciting contemporary crafts from both emerging and established designer/makers. The warm ambience and decadent charm that greets you, when you open the door of Heart Gallery, encourages you to browse the ambitious programme of ever-changing showcases and exhibitions and to discover a haven from the predictability of the High Street. Heart Gallery is a beautiful place, in a beautiful town and loves all things beautiful and once discovered, it's never forgotten. Heart Gallery also incorporates three studios, which offer you the opportunity to meet Heart Gallery's resident designer/makers in leather-work, jewellery and textiles and to appreciate their expertise in creating new designs and commissioned pieces.

Heart Gallery

Catherine Edwards

Bold, elegant bags, satchels and accessories, made using only the finest British saddlery leathers, created as exclusive designs or one off commissions.

Originally trained as a bespoke boot and shoemaker, Catherine uses many of the skills she gained to give her leather goods the added appeal of being made entirely by hand.

Nikki Rose

Nikki Rose creates bespoke textile accessories for the home and wardrobe. She blends a treasure trove of delicious fabrics – French vintage, locally produced tweed and moleskin, junk shop finds and re-cycled clothes - transforming them into sumptuous embroidered lampshades, handbags, corsages, cushions and wall pieces, making her work sustainable and beautiful.

Clare Lupino

Specialising in transforming vintage jewellery into stunning, bespoke contemporary designs, Clare Lupino can even include sentimental pieces of family jewellery, to create awe-inspiring heirlooms. Semi-precious stones are reworked with 1920s crystals, 30s dressclips, 40s pearls, 50s earrings and themed brooches from the 1960s into one-off tiaras, neckpieces, wristcuffs and earrings.

Heart Gallery

Clockwise from top left:
Rozie Keogh – *wirework*; Timea Sido – *ceramics*;
Emily Morgan – *jewellery*; Rosemary Wright – *wood*;
Kate Rhodes – *jewellery*

Heart Gallery

Joanna Haines

Joanna Haines' jewellery is a personal celebration, transforming unwanted vintage glass buttons into contemporary pieces that bring forth a smile of recognition. Her jewellery is unusual with no two pieces the same, as she sources misplaced, lost and donated glass buttons. Joanna's jewellery range incorporates many different pieces; from funky all button chokers, to frivolous single buttons on ribbon.

Janine Partington

Janine Partington is a Bristol-based enamel artist who exhibits across the UK. Taking inspiration from the forms of trees, leaves, seedheads and landscape, her designs use the traditional medium of enamel in a thoroughly contemporary way.

Janine hand cuts intricate stencils which she then arranges on prepared copper and sifts over with enamel powder. Each piece is then fired in a kiln at 800°C. This process is repeated until the image is complete. By virtue of the process no two images will be identical. Their durability and inability to fade make them an ideal adornment to all the rooms of any house or workspace including bathrooms, kitchens and conservatories.

Tamsin Howells

The process used in this contemporary jewellery is a lamination technique which uses resin to trap fabric in between plastic. The specially designed hinge provides ease of use. Recycling old and vintage fabrics plays an important role in Tamsin's work. Materials such as sweet wrappers, men's shirts, ties and vintage fabrics that date from the 1920s-1950s making each piece a one-off or part of a limited edition.

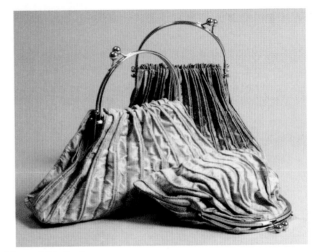

Clare Webster

Clare Webster individually creates textile accessories using techniques originally conceived in the making of textile sculptures. With simple stitch techniques she creates sculptural fabric forms through the repetition of pleats and tucks. Creating movement and giving structure to plain coloured cloths that dictate their own shape.

The finest hand woven silk is machine stitched to enhance shadow and texture within the fabric. These luxurious accessories are reminiscent of antique bodices, crinolines and corsetry. The designs are nostalgic and also exciting and contemporary with every piece created to be functional and beautiful.

Clare designs and makes a range of handbags, scarves, wraps and men's ties and has also undertaken numerous commissions including interior furnishings. Her work is elegant and refined and the designs complement her choice of fabrics completely.

Sanders & Wallace

Andrew and David established one of the first British glass studios in 1978. From their present workshop in Pateley Bridge they produce a range of pieces in recycled lead crystal using traditional English glassmaking techniques. Their range includes vases, bowls, paperweights and drinking glasses, but it is for their perfume bottle collection that they are best known.

Ruth Bridges

Working in silver and 18 carat gold, Brighton based jeweller Ruth Bridges combines high quality craftsmanship with contemporary design to create distinctive jewellery. Her inspiration is drawn from the natural world, particularly rock formations smoothed and hollowed by time. The smooth, tactile forms that recur in her jewellery are complimented by the exquisite detail of tiny diamonds and contrasting metal.

Lund Gallery

Alne Road, Near Easingwold
North Yorkshire, YO61 3PA
*Open: Thursday–Saturday 11am–5pm,
Sunday and Bank Holidays–noon–4pm. Closed during January*

P C 0% ♿

T: 01347 824400
E:info@lundgallery.co.uk
www.lundgallery.co.uk

Lund Gallery is housed in a converted dairy on a small-holding outside the market town of Easingwold, just 20 minutes drive north from York. The open aspect makes it an ideal space for exhibiting art in an uncluttered and relaxing environment.

The gallery offers a wide range of contemporary paintings, ceramics and sculpture from regional and national makers and hosts up to six solo or themed exhibitions a year. We usually have work in stock by Sam Hall, Peter Hayes, Eddie Curtis, Ruth King, Steph Black, Jane Blackman, RAMP Ceramics and resident landscape artist Debbie Loane.

Clockwise from top left:
Steph Black; Geoffrey Bradford – *mixed media*; Ruth King; Eddie Curtis; Sam Hall

Manchester Craft & Design Centre

17 Oak Street, Northern Quarter
Manchester M4 5JD
Open: Monday-Saturday 10am-5.30pm plus Sundays in December

T: 0161 832 4274
E: info@craftanddesign.com
www.craftanddesign.com

P C ☕

Located in Manchester city centre's Northern Quarter, Manchester Craft and Design Centre is at the hub of a growing innovative and artistic community. It is the largest combined retail and production centre for the north west's top designer/makers and is one of the few places in the UK open to the public, where contemporary goods are individually produced and sold on the premises. Formerly a Victorian fish market, the centre houses two floors of shops, ranging from jewellery, sculpture and textiles to ceramics and accessory design.

Many of the artists at the Manchester Craft and Design Centre exhibit at prestigious trade fairs such as Origin, 100% Design and Top Drawer. All work is for sale and individual commissions are welcomed.

The centre also hosts a contemporary craft exhibitions programme of around four exhibitions a year, showcasing the work of both emerging and established national and international makers. Hungry shoppers can relax in the open-plan Café Aromat, and enjoy delicious home-cooked food in inspiring surroundings.

Liz Chamberlain
(working within Jo Lavelle's studio)

As a designer/maker of jewellery, Liz aims to experiment with traditional jewellery-making techniques, such as reticulation, to maintain a delicate feel to the surface of the material.

   Inspired by organic textures and form, her work is both elegant and simple. Liz works mostly with silver, sometimes oxidising the surface for contrast, to create a wide range of jewellery pieces.

Suzanne Devine

Since completing her degree in Embroidery at Manchester Metropolitan University, Suzanne has been developing the use of leather into functional items. Following her original range of mini-bags, she has progressed her work to larger, practical bags, wallets and purses for men and women, using soft lambs leather and cow hide. Her range of rich colours, combined with traditional use of embroidery techniques has helped create a range of products that appeal to many individuals. Suzanne works in her intimate studio space, showcasing her work and taking on individual commissions for customers.

The March Hare Craft Gallery

C ☕

1 Ripon Small Shops, Duck Hill
Ripon, North Yorkshire HG4 1BL
Open: Monday-Saturday 10am-5pm, Sunday 11am-4pm

T: 01765 608833
E: Carnie123@aol.com

Set in the heart of the historic part of Ripon, minutes away from the cathedral, The March Hare Craft Gallery is nestled away in a Victorian style arcade, which once was the city's Temperance Hall.

The Gallery has a reputation as the place to find something unusual and of quality. You will find affordable, exceptional, handmade art and craft in a welcoming and friendly atmosphere.

Work is on sale with a rolling showcase and exhibition programme. Along with established makers from all around Britain, we encourage local artists and emerging new talent to contact us.

Visitors are welcome to add their name to our mailing list for advance notice of our exhibitions and an invite to our exhibition previews. The Visitor comments speak for themselves:
'A wonderful Gallery in a wonderful city!'
'Delightful – all articles are beautifully selected and presented. How creative people can be!'
'Lovely! A visual feast!',
'I love coming here', 'Every visit here is a delight!'
'A great place to find unusual and beautiful things in a friendly atmosphere!'
'modern & refined very tasteful. A pleasure to visit'

The March Hare Craft Gallery

Moira McTague

Moira McTague is a painter and etcher. Her work is inspired by favourite objects and her immediate surroundings. She works from life, often using recurrent themes, developing an intimate understanding of her subject matter. The processes of painting and etching are those of discovery and one of her aims is to create a balance and harmony. She has exhibited widely including in the Laing Landscape Exhibition and The National Print Exhibition, Mall Galleries, London. Moira's beautiful owl, hare and Auricula etchings are often shown at The March Hare Gallery

Tina Free

Tina designs and makes jewellery using silver, gold, glass, semi-precious stones and fresh water pearls. Upon receiving commissions from the famous Tate Gallery and The National Gallery, London, Tina has created fabulous jewellery to complement paintings from some of the most famous painters in the world.

You can see an exclusive collection of her beautiful jewellery at the March Hare Gallery, designed in the Alice in Wonderland theme. The pieces include Queen of Hearts, The White Rabbit and Alice through the looking glass etc.

Platform Gallery

Station Road, Clitheroe
Lancashire BB7 2JT
Open: Monday-Saturday 10am-4.30pm.
Please contact for other times

0% ♿

T: 01200 443071/414556
E: platform.gallery@ribblevalley.gov.uk
www.ribblevalley.gov.uk/platformgallery

The Platform Gallery is situated in the historic market town of Clitheroe, Lancashire, and is run by Ribble Valley Borough Council. The gallery is located in a prime position in the old railway station building, built in 1870. The gallery was awarded an Arts Lottery Grant in 2001 and was totally refurbished to provide an airy contemporary craft exhibition space, shop and education facilities.

The Platform Gallery hosts an exciting and varied programme of exhibitions throughout the year, including solo, group and touring shows. The emphasis is on high quality and innovative work by both national and local makers.

The gallery shop features a wide and ever-changing selection of ceramics, glass, wood, textiles and jewellery to suit all budgets. Our experienced staff can also help with special orders and commissions.

The gallery provides craft workshops and talks for all ages and abilities, throughout the year.

Photo: John Toms

Platform Gallery

James Hake

I work at the potter's wheel, specialising in large bowls and one off pieces. I also make slab rolled pieces such as wall hangings and square dishes.

Inspired by Oriental ceramics, I have developed a range of stoneware glazes fired in a gas kiln. Glazes are applied quickly by dipping and pouring in different combinations, which fuse together in the heat of the kiln. Firing has become an increasingly creative part of my making cycle. During each firing, I carefully control the temperature and atmosphere of the kiln, to achieve the colours and surface qualities I am searching for.

Carol Hill

I started making glass beads in 2002, after taking a class in America. I was hooked and couldn't wait to get back home and set up my own studio. Taking my inspiration from flowers and nature, I enjoy the ability to create depth and interest using encasing and layering on my beads. I use mainly Italian effetre glass rods, although more and more glass is becoming available to the glass bead maker. The possibilities are endless, with different effects appearing with the combination of different colours. The beads are made using a mixed fuel torch and then annealed to make sure they will be strong and no stress remains within them. I make them up into jewellery using only sterling silver components, with the exception of my bookstrings.

Pyramid Gallery

43 Stonegate
York YO1 8AW
Open: Everyday 10am-5pm, Sunday 11am-4.30pm

C0%

T: 01904 641187
E: pyramidgallery2004@yahoo.co.uk
www.pyramidgallery.com

Pyramid Gallery is a privately owned shop and gallery in the heart of medieval York, close to The Minster. Established in 1980, Pyramid offers one of the country's finest selections of British made contemporary crafts, jewellery and original prints, enthusiastically displayed in a fifteenth century building that is owned by the National Trust.

A member of the Independent Craft Galleries Association, the gallery displays work by many leading British designers including over 50 jewellers plus printmakers, sculptors, potters, wood workers and glass makers. Displays are constantly changing and the two first floor galleries are used for exhibitions which are presented in detail on the web site.

Pyramid can be found on Stonegate, which is one of York's best known and prettiest shopping streets running between the south door of the Minster and Betty's cafe on St. Helens Square. Three great attractions five minutes apart, but allow at least half a day! And we'll look after your purchases for you while you queue at Betty's.

Ann W. Baxter

Trained at Leeds College of Art, Ann is a sculptor working mainly in wood and stone, and sometimes, bronze. She prefers to use timber from renewable sources but also has a stock of exotic woods that she has stored for many years.

All her carvings are complete one-offs and are carved using hand tools. Some pieces are painted or stained but always allow the character of the wood to show. Her main subjects are horses and farm animals, birds and British wild animals.

Ann is a long standing member of the Society of Equestrian Artists with whom she has exhibited regularly, winning several awards including The President's Medal and the British Sporting Art Trust award.

Paul Jenkins

Paul Jenkins was born in the West Midlands in 1949, and first started his career in art in the early 70's sculpting in wood and then found himself drawn to sculpting in clay and wax. He then went on to study ceramics at Dudley College of Art.

After graduating in 1979 he set up his own business designing and manufacturing Sculpture and Ceramics, which was then sold all over the world.

Paul has also created works for The National Trust and various other organisations. Paul's inspiration comes from his love of nature, especially animals. Many of his pieces are inspired from direct observations of wild animals in their natural habitat.

Radiance

P C

58, Market Street, Hebden Bridge
West Yorkshire HX7 6AA
Open: Wednesday-Saturday 11am-5pm, Sunday 11am-4pm

T: 01422 845764
E: hannah@radiancelighting.co.uk
www.radiancelighting.co.uk

Hannah Nunn started her artistic life making intricate hand-cut parchment lamps and supplying craft galleries across the country. Along the way, she has fallen in love with the work of many other designer/makers, who also use light to bring their craft to life. In 2005 she set up Radiance to bring these makers together into one glowing space. The result is delicate, decadent and dazzling!

Set in Hebden Bridge, famous for its independent shops, cafés and an artistic community, Radiance brings together local and national light makers, in a warm and inviting space.

Visitors appreciate the diverse collection of styles, materials and wonderfully innovative ideas!

Hannah's lamp making workshop is adjacent to the gallery and she and many of the other artists are happy to fulfil personal commissions.

Hannah Nunn

I make parchment table lamps, wall lamps, pendant shades and exquisite strings of fairy lights. My designs are inspired by the beauty and simplicity of nature. They are created by a process of cutting, layering, laminating, and then adding light.

I love the way the light works with the paper, accentuating the crisp lines and peeping through the tiny pinpricks. When I'm designing, I use a translucent cutting mat on a light table. Cutting into the paper is like drawing with light and is very satisfying.

I have my workshop at Radiance where my whole range is permanently on display.

Amy Cooper

I make organic porcelain forms for subtle illumination. The pieces are largely inspired by natural spaces and objects. I am intrigued by the endless variations in nature and the idea of an ongoing evolutionary process of adaptation. All of my porcelain work is slipcast and each piece is individually manipulated when it is still soft. Textured glazes, slips and diamond polishing create some unexpected and enticing surfaces. The work is fired in either an electric or gas kiln to create various colours of translucency in the finished pieces.

I am a member of Red Herring Studios which is a mixed discipline group based in Hove, East Sussex.

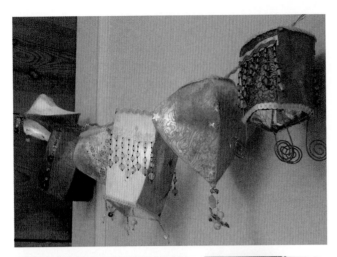

Clockwise from top left:
Louise Traill – *paper*; Wendy Jung –
ceramics; Colin Chetwood – *metal/paper*;
Nikki Rose – *hand painted silk shades*;
Emerald Faerie – *wire & found objects*

Donna Morrow – mixed textiles page 315

Wensley Gallery

6-8 Market Place
Ramsbottom, Bury
Lancashire BL0 9HT
Open: Monday-Saturday 10am-5pm, Sunday 10am-4pm

c &

T: 01706 824772
E: staff@wensleygallery.co.uk
www.wensleygallery.co.uk

The Wensley Gallery is housed in a grade II listed building in the heart of Ramsbottom, a bustling unspoiled Lancashire village with many specialist shops and a variety of places to eat, just 12 miles north of Manchester.

Within the gallery's 2,000 square feet you will find an extensive range of original art to suit all pockets and tastes. With paintings, embroidery, woodturning, ceramics, metal sculpture and jewellery almost every medium is represented. Having four general exhibitions and up to 60 individual exhibitions each year the gallery is constantly changing, and introduces new artists throughout the year. Everything in the gallery is hand crafted so you are sure find a truly individual addition for your home or a special gift.

Ramsbottom provides a wonderful day out for visitors. Peel Tower and Holcombe Hill provide breathtaking views of the surrounding countryside. For those wishing to combine a love of walking with art there is the Irwell Sculpture Trail, the largest public art scheme in the UK, with one of the major works, the Tilted Vase outside the Wensley Gallery. There is also the East Lancashire Steam Railway connecting the village with Bury and Rawtenstall.

Andy Beck

Andy's work is largely motivated by the found and recycled materials he uses to create his striking sculptures. Just one small piece from an old engine or perhaps a discarded tool can evolve into whole new and interesting character.

   Whether a six foot rock star or tiny hedgehog desperately attempting DIY, Andy's work never fails to surprise and delight. Much of his work has a minimalist quality, but he often includes small details which are only discovered after taking a much closer look, and it is this understated humour and attention to detail which has enchanted so many.

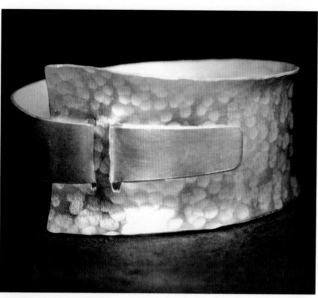

Barbara Webster

Working with precious metals enables forms to emerge and change before your eyes; intense heat allows the imagination to play freely. Some pieces start out with a precise outline, but within this there are more organic forms. Discs and rectangles are softened by annealing and reticulation, leaving a texture like hoar frost. Necklaces can twist and taper, evolving as they are worked upon. A sinuous line has great appeal, as has a textured finish, which can bear the marks of the process of making.

   Bangles and rings are inspired by anglo-saxon finds, given a simple line, to present clarity of form. Matisse, always the most decorative of fine artists, has provided the basis for the birds which are included in some of my pieces.

Rene Cryer

Rene's work manifests in many forms, creating a wide range of ceramic pieces including dishes, mirrors, water features, tables, vases and sculptures. Her work is decorative rather than functional and can have a range of finishes – shiny, matt, satin and even painted with a stone-like paint.

Much of her work is inspired by plant life, birds and fish, giving her ceramics an organic character both in form and colour. Rene has a personal style which is instantly recognisable, and collected by many, and is constantly coming up with new ideas – so look out for them.

Yvonne Wright

My interest in ceramics began when I joined evening classes as an adult student which eventually led to me gaining a degree, in 3D design from Manchester University.

Having worked with different ceramic processes, it was raku that excited me. Most of my work is quite delicate and due to this many pieces are prone to breakages and cracking. But it is the contrast between the glazed and smoked surfaces, sometimes metallic and lustres appear by magic. It is the risk and the uncertainty that make raku so exciting.

Wensley Gallery

Rob MIller

Rob Miller is a prolific painter, working mainly in acrylics and mixed media. His style is an intriguing combination of realism and abstraction. He portrays the beauty of the European landscape and the place of human habitation in it. He studied art at the University of Bolton. Rob Miller is now painting full time and undertaking an MA in fine Art.

Sunita Limaye

Sculptures, vessels, bespoke tiles, mirrors and wall plaques. A rarely seen process of fusing glass to ceramic providing a depth of colour and vibrancy, not seen in glazes alone.

Wensley Gallery

Geoff Nuttall

Geoff was born in 1937 in Bury, and his family moved to Oldham in 1939. At the age of 13 he won a scholarship for Oldham School of Art leaving at 15 to start work as an apprentice poster artist.

Interest in painting was mixed with other hobbies until at 18 Geoff did two years National Service. Following that he worked in Manchester at a publicity and display firm.

Geoff is married with two sons living in Shuttleworth, Ramsbottom. In 1962 he started his own business in Bury as a poster artist. Geoff's interest in watercolours increased, working in the evenings and weekends from his own photographs mainly of local subjects plus Lakeland scenes with a special love of old bridges. Now retired he can work when he likes.

Norman Eames

My work was inspired from an experiment I conducted several years ago with twigs and resin. I found the combination, when sectioned, to be very pleasing and realised it had potential artistically. I have since developed the techniques involved and now produce a range of pieces with a common theme.

All my work utilises the mediums of wood and resin to produce a wide range of effects, combining the natural beauty of wood. from natural twig or log sections and commercially available hardwoods, with the brilliant colour possibilities available from pigmented resins.

All my work is original and hand made and includes functional items, such as coasters and candle holders, to the purely artistic sculptures and pictures.

Wensley Gallery

Wendy Elliott

Wendy always loved experimenting with different materials and enjoyed the satisfying process of making things out of scraps of fabric.

Later she studied a variety of art forms, which included ceramics, creative textiles and embroidery. Enjoying working with textiles and ceramics Wendy began the exciting process of trying to marry the two. Over the years, her work has become more mixed media, incorporating wires, sequins and glass, hand-made paper and felt. Wendy has drawn her inspiration from a wide range of subjects including stained glass windows, seascapes and building. More recently she has been inspired by the rich designs and textures in Islamic art, which she admired on her recent visits to India and Pakistan.

Sue Jenkins

After many years of working with clay, mainly as slabs or tiles, I changed direction on discovering a lovely coarse textured clay suitable for firing to stoneware temperatures and therefore suitable for going outside. My work recently has been mainly animals and birds but I am now exploring other more organic forms inspired by nature, and using clays to which colours and extra textures have been added for decorative effects.

Wensley Gallery

Daryl Hing
East and West Jewellery Company

East and West Jewellery Company produces necklaces, bracelets and earrings using a combination of Nepalese silver beads, Tibetan semi-precious stones, crystal gemstones, freshwater pearls and vintage beads.

For centuries beads have been used to define culture and our aim is to bring together the spirit of eastern and western culture in the designs of our individually crafted pieces.

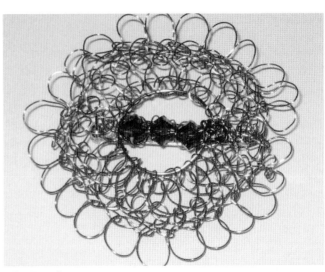

Liz Davies

I am a contemporary jewellery designer living near Lancaster. Designing jewellery came through my final project whilst on a BA hons in international textile design and surface pattern in 1999. I specialised in textile art.
My final project based on Victorian costume and accessories inspired the theme. This led me to develop and experiment with different techniques to create elaborate neckpieces and these led to commissions through family, friends and galleries.

My latest collection is inspired by nature. I hand knit my pieces using different sizes of needles and enamelled wires, to create one-off pieces of art, which are functional and wearable as jewellery pieces. I sew on by hand Swarovski Crystals and Freshwater Pearls, which shimmer with the light.

NE England, Lake District & Scotland

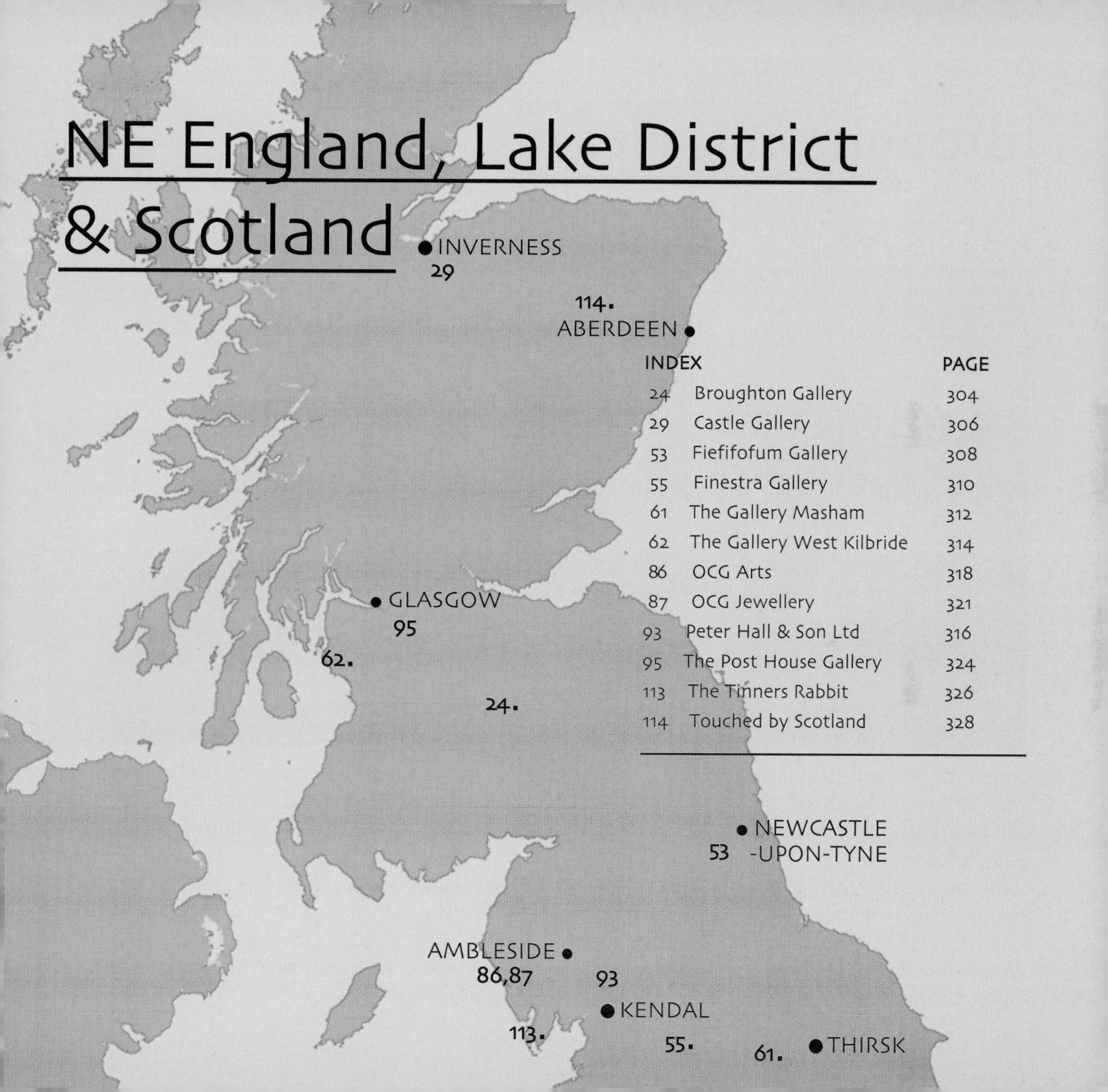

● INVERNESS
29

114 ■

ABERDEEN ●

● GLASGOW
95

62 ■

24 ■

● NEWCASTLE
53 -UPON-TYNE

AMBLESIDE ●
86,87   93

113 ■

● KENDAL

55 ■   61 ■ ● THIRSK

Broughton Gallery

P C 0%

Broughton Place,
Broughton
Scotland ML12 6HJ
Open: Wednesday-Sunday 10.30am-5pm during exhibitions

T: 01899 830234
E: info@broughtongallery.co.uk
www.broughtongallery.co.uk

Photo: Marius Alexander

Broughton Gallery, just north of the village of Broughton in the Scottish Borders, occupies the ground floor of Broughton Place, one of the last of Britain's large houses to be built in the traditional style. The house was designed by the young Basil Spence in the style of a Scottish tower house and was completed in 1938.

It is appropriate, given Sir Basil Spence's belief in the important role played by art and crafts in 'humanising' buildings, that part of Broughton Place should be given over to their promotion.

In its 32nd year, Broughton Gallery continues to provide a showcase for exceptional and competitively-priced contemporary art and crafts. Much of the work is sourced from Scotland but the watchword for Broughton Gallery is 'quality' from wherever it is sourced.

Photos 1 & 5 by Shannon Tofts

Clockwise from top left:
Trevor Leat – *willow;*
Bethan Lloyd Worthington
– *porcelain;*
Charlotte Cadzow –
earthenware;
Diane King – *jewellery;*
Ruth King – *salt-glazed;*
Judith Gregson –
stone carving

Broughton Gallery

Castle Gallery

43 Castle Street
Inverness IV2 3DU
Open: Monday-Saturday 9am-5pm

P C 0%

T: 01463 729512
E: info@castlegallery.co.uk
www.castlegallery.co.uk

The Castle Gallery was described in the Independent newspaper as one of the best reasons to visit Inverness. It is one of the leading galleries in Scotland and has an enviable reputation for the quality of its artists and innovation of its shows. The staff are friendly and very informative, being able to provide details on any of the artists featured.

The gallery shows figurative, landscape and abstract work by artists from Scotland and throughout Britain. The constantly changing exhibitions feature paintings, sculpture, hand-made prints, contemporary applied arts and designer jewellery. With work by established artists and emerging talent, the Castle Gallery provides a welcoming environment where visitors may browse, enjoy and purchase the best in contemporary art.

Maureen Minchin – *ceramic plate & painted bird detail*

Castle Gallery

Clockwise from top left:
Alisdair McKay – *wood;*
Blandine Anderson – *ceramic;*
Anne-Marie Robinson – *ceramic;*
Scott Irvine – *wood/glass* & Miranda Sharpe – *silver*

Castle Gallery

Fifiefofum

Westside Farm, Newton, Nr Corbridge
Northumberland NE43 7TW
Open: Wednesday-Saturday 10am-5pm, Sunday 11am-5pm

T: 01661 843778
E: info@fifiefofum.com
www.fifiefofum.com

Situated in the beautiful Tyne Valley, three miles from Corbridge and only 15 miles (20 minutes) from Newcastle, fifiefofum is a special place to visit.

Fifiefofum is a welcoming and friendly gallery situated on a small 150 acre estate in a redundant farm shed, covering over 600 sq metres. With one of the finest, uninterrupted views across the Tyne Valley, the light and airy space is ideal for exhibiting artwork;

A rolling exhibition programme runs throughout the year, bringing new and exciting artwork from local and national artists.Fifiefofum also runs a wide range of creative workshops and events throughout the year utilising the surrounding landscaped grounds and lakeside setting.

Curator and resident artist, Sue Moffitt runs the gallery with her husband, graphic designer and photographer, Roy Sturgeon. Sue's daughter, Lucy Moffitt makes contemporary jewellery and manages the day to day running of the gallery.

The gallery offers a diverse selection of original paintings, prints, ceramics, glass, sculpture, jewellery, textiles, etchings, wood, photography, limited edition prints and more. Sue's cow paintings have become popular in the UK and overseas, and her studio resides in the gallery.

Clockwise from top left:
Sue Moffitt; Lucy Moffitt; Chris Mouncey; Morag Gordon – *glass*; Alan Stones – *lithographs* & William Wilson – *Highland cow sculpture* Opposite page: Views of the gallery & activities

Fifiefofum

Finestra Gallery

P C

12 Main Street
Kirkby Lonsdale
Cumbria LA6 2AE
Open: 10am-5pm, Sunday 11am-5pm all year

T: 015242 73747
E: info@finestragallery.co.uk
www.finestragallery.co.uk

Finestra Gallery is set in the beautiful historic Market Town of Kirkby Lonsdale on the edge of the Lake District, and was opened in November 2003 by artist William H. Jones and his wife Bernadette. From the beginning, the idea of exhibiting only original paintings was very important to them. This has quickly attracted a number of highly established British artists, and a good reputation has been earned. A diverse exhibition programme ensures an exciting visit at any time of the year; and the website has a full calendar of current and upcoming exhibitions. The gallery's aim is to offer space for a wide range of artists who produce work of exceptional high quality.

Artists: William H. Jones, David Allen, Martin Greenland, Fiona Clucas, Vivienne Pooley, James Wheeler, David C Lyons, Thuline De Cock, Christopher Fry and Libby Edmondson
Ceramics: Christine Cummings, Sue Bartholomew, Roger Cockram, Annie Peaker, Mark Smith, James Hake, Elaine Peto and Nick Mackman.
Bronze: Paul Jenkins and Libby Edmondson

Clockwise from top left:
James Hake;
Christine Romano – *fused glass;*
Christine Cummings;
Annie Peaker & Della Clark

Finestra Gallery

The Gallery Masham

P C 0% ♿

24 Market Place, Masham
Ripon, North Yorkshire HG4 4EB
Open: Tuesday-Saturday 10am-5pm, Sunday 1-5pm

T: 01765 689554
E: enquiry@mashamgallery.co.uk
www.mashamgallery.co.uk

Situated in Masham's beautiful Georgian Market Place since 1994. The Gallery is a lively and colourful artist-run space, exhibiting established and emerging artists and crafts-people. Two light rooms exhibit exceptional work- functional and fun ceramics, groovy glass and serious sculpture amongst many other unusual pieces. Adorning the walls are original paintings and limited edition prints. A Hayvend machine also adds interest - vending unusual contemporary art at only £2.

Themed exhibitions are held around three times a year, details on the website. The Gallery has recently added an exciting new toy room. Not surprisingly it has it's own quirky style with photographic grass tiles on the floor and clouds and birds on the ceiling. The room houses some of the best in traditional and innovative wooden and fairly

traded toys. A play table, art materials and a children's gallery are provided for our younger customers.

The Gallery Masham

Clockwise from top left:

Hester Cox – *collagraph*; Glover & Smith – *Pewter leaf salt bowl*; Sally Page – *fused glass*;
Simon Griffiths – *ceramics* & Sue Sharp – *ceramics*

Masham Gallery

The Gallery West Kilbride

P C ♿

75/77 Main Street, West Kilbride
Craft Town
North Ayrshire KA23 9AP
Open: Tuesday-Saturday 10am-4pm (during exhibitions)

T: 01294 829179
E: info@westkilbride.org.uk
www.westkilbride.org.uk

Exhibition by Caroline Dear – *mixed media, grass, rushes & heather*

The Craft Town was Winner of Enterprising Britain and a SURF Award in 2006

Situated against rolling hills on the rugged North Ayrshire coast overlooking the Isle of Arran, West Kilbride is home to Craft Town Scotland. A registered charity and social enterprise established in 1998 by the local community, the aim to become Scotland's first craft town was endorsed by the Scottish Parliament in 2000.

Situated in this picturesque small town is a contemporary gallery and five craft studios, with three new studios due to open in 2007. Highlighting the diverse range of quality craft produced by contemporary designer-makers, Craft Town Scotland offers an opportunity to see and buy quality work in one easily accessible location.

The Gallery, a light and airy exhibition space, occupies a prime site within the Main Street and is a focus for Craft Town Scotland. Programmes of temporary exhibitions show the work of professional designer-makers from the UK and also endeavour to support emerging talent, regularly featuring the work of graduates from the UK's Art colleges.

The West Kilbride studios each have a small gallery area with maker's workshop, which present visitors with the prospect of enjoying beautifully crafted objects whilst meeting the creators.

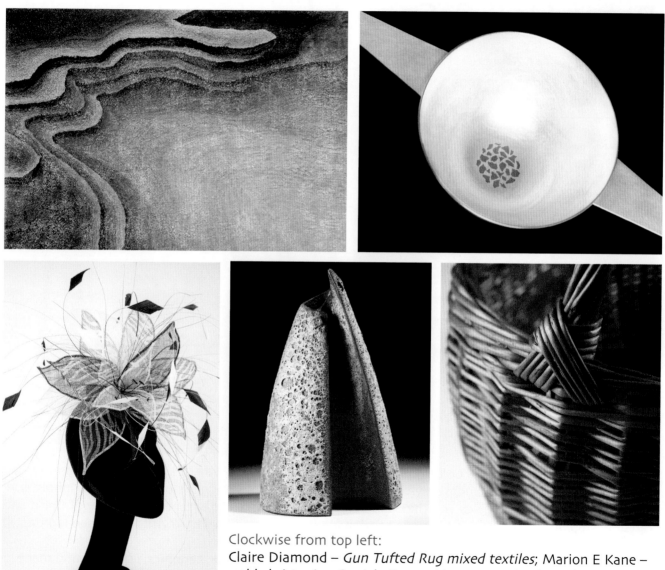

Clockwise from top left:
Claire Diamond – *Gun Tufted Rug mixed textiles*; Marion E Kane – *gold christening Quaich*; Donna Morrow – *mixed textiles*;
Maggie Broadley – *stoneware*; Virgil Bauzys – *Somerset willow*

The Gallery West Kilbride

Peter Hall & Son Ltd.

Danes Road, Staveley
Kendal, Cumbria LA8 9PL
Open: Monday-Friday 9am-5pm, Saturday from Easter 10am-4pm,
Saturday Christmas-Easter 10am-1pm

P C &

T: 01539 821633
E: info@peter-hall.co.uk
www.peter-hall.co.uk

Photo:Jeremy Hall

Situated in the bustling village of Staveley, near Kendal, Peter Hall & Son Ltd. was established in 1972, as cabinet makers, it now includes services in restoration, interior design, woodturning and upholstery.

A visit to the showroom gives you the opportunity to experience the exceptional quality of finish and craftsmanship. All the furniture is designed and made on the premises where visitors can see highly skilled craftsmen at work.

The showroom also features a variety of woodturning, lighting, glass, ceramics, leather, hand made candles and more. Jeremy Hall comments, "We work closely with our clients to create individual pieces which last generations."

Jo Vincent

Jo Vincent Glass Designers are based on the edge of the beautiful English Lake District. They specialise in creating customised glass solutions for commercial and private spaces. They create architectural glass and interior accessories including:
lighting, door handles, balustrades, table tops, splash backs and vessels.

The studio utilises a variety of glass making techniques, creating designs rich in textures and colours suitable for the interior or exterior.

They offer a bespoke design and manufacturing service, producing one-off glass features for a range of clients alongside a, ready to buy, collection.

Liz Cameron

Liz Cameron obtained a BA hons degree in ceramics from Wolverhampton followed by five years in Hong Kong where she gained experience in glazes and the form of her ceramics.

Now living and working in South Lanarkshire, she uses stoneware clay to make a range of hand thrown functional domestic ceramics, ranging from ovenware dishes to dinner plates.

Peter Hall & Son Ltd

OCG Arts

Old Courthouse Gallery, Market Place
Ambleside, Cumbria LA22 9BU
*Open: Daily 10am-5pm, Closed: Christmas Day, Boxing Day,
New Year's Day & August Bank Holiday Monday*

T: 015394 32022
E: andrew@ocg-arts.com
www.ocg-arts.com

Photography by ward

Set in the busy market town of Ambleside amidst the stunning scenery of the Lakes District, OCG has over the past 14 years become one of the most respected and well known galleries in the north of England.

The spacious gallery displays on three floors all that is best in contemporary British art and design by some of the countries' leading and up and coming designer makers, the emphasis being on high quality craftsmanship and individuality.

OCG has a diverse and wonderful range of glass, ceramics, turned wood, furniture, metal work, bronze sculpture, original paintings and limited edition prints, textiles (embroidery and painted silk).

Clockwise from
top left:
Anthony Scott – *bronze;*
Jane Smith, Virginia
Dowe & Sarah Vernon
all – *ceramics &*
Libby Edmondson –
bronze resin

Clockwise from
top left :
Philip Hearsey –
bronze sculpture,
Hannah Turner –
ceramics,
Sly Glass &
Chris Comins – *glass*

OCG Arts

OCG Jewellery

Market Place
Ambleside, Cumbria LA22 9BU
*Open: Daily 10am-5pm, Closed: Christmas Day, Boxing Day,
New Year's Day & August Bank Holiday Monday*

T:015394 33866
E: info@ocgjewellery.com
www.ocgjewellery.com

Photography by ward

OCG Jewellery has gone from strength to strength in the past four years; building on its reputation for exciting contemporary work with great design and quality, in a relaxed and friendly atmosphere.

Our jewellery ranges from beautiful, eminently wearable silver with diamonds and semi-precious stones; vibrant acrylics and resin, through to the wonderful Tahitian and South Sea pearls of Lilian Busch, sensational natural coloured diamonds set in platinum or gold and the perfect D Flawless collection by international designer Paul Spurgeon.

OCG Jewellery

Clockwise from top left:
Alan Ardiff, Becky Crow, Nick Hubbard & Rowena Park

OCG Jewellery

Clockwise from top left:
Andrew Geoghegan, Ian Henderson, Paul Spurgeon, David Smith & Michael Carpenter

OCG Jewellery

The Post House Gallery

83 Glasgow Road
Blanefield,
Glasgow G63 9HP
Open: Tuesday-Saturday 10am-5.30pm

T: 01360 771544
E: info@theposthousegallery.co.uk
www.theposthousegallery.co.uk

The Post House Gallery opened in 2005 in the picturesque village of Blanefield situated at the foot of the Campsie Fells. The gallery has retained the original 1893 shop fittings of the former General Store and Post Office, which provides an ideal backdrop to display an eclectic range of crafts.

The Post House Gallery has quickly established a reputation for unusual pieces sourced both locally and internationally. With a jeweller/silversmith and ceramicist working within this family business, the addition of a new workshop behind the gallery has allowed designs to be developed and made on the premises. The gallery is currently planning exhibitions in a variety of media to be held throughout the year.

Wendy Kershaw

Wendy Kershaw creates very detailed narrative illustrations on porcelain, in the form of framed tiles, jewellery and vessels. Each piece is intricately etched with needles, combining bold composition with the subtle details.

The narratives include folk sayings and everyday life celebrated in its full importance, resulting in a rich visual storytelling that is at once quirky, dark and humorous.

Wendy graduated with first class honours from Gray's School of Art in Aberdeen followed by an MA in Ceramics at Cardiff.
Illustration:
Ben has only one pair of chopsticks – on porcelain

Below from the left:
Tait & Style
Abbott & Ellwood – *metal*
McGonigle Glass

The Post House Gallery

The Tinners' Rabbit

50 Market Street, Ulverston
Cumbria LA12 7LS
Open: Monday-Saturday 9.30am-5pm

T: 01229 588808
E: tinnersrabbit@btinternet.com
www.tinnersrabbitulverston.co.uk

The Tinners' Rabbit just can't let the grass grow under his feet!

This year, Chris is buying number 52 Market Street (next door down) and transferring 'Two by Two' ladies clothing into there. The picture framing currently in the gallery will move into number 54 vacated by 'Two by Two', and a small coffee bar will be established within the gallery in the space vacated by the picture framing! Phew!

Visitors will still find the 'affordable art' that distinguishes The Tinners' Rabbit and an on-going calendar of exhibitions of interesting artists from throughout the UK and beyond.

Clockwise from top left:
Ken & Valerie Shelton; Mark Halliday; Dresser with spongeware by – Emma Bridgewater, English Country Pottery, Nicholas Mosse; Krukker – *sculptural ceramics;* Libby Edmondson – *ceramics*

Touched by Scotland

P C ☕ ♿

The Village of Oyne
Ryehill, Oyne
Aberdeenshire AB52 6QS
Open: Monday-Saturday 10am-5pm, Sunday 1pm-5pm

T: 01464 851489
info@touchedbyscotland.com
www.touchedbyscotland.com

Touched By Scotland Ltd sits at the foot of the hill of Bennachie in the rural village of Oyne, Aberdeenshire. Bennachie has long been considered the centre stone of Scotland's largest county and, as can be seen in the gallery, has been an inspiration to the artists and craftspeople of the North East.

Touched By Scotland Ltd was established in 2003 to promote, encourage, and support local artisans in and around North East. Scotland. The business has grown to become known as the place to find unusual handcrafted goods. Over 300 artists display and sell their work at the gallery most of which is Scottish based. You will also find work from established artists from outwith the area. The company prides itself on attention to detail and customer service. A regular schedule of exhibitions highlights work by emerging and established artists.

The owners of Touched By Scotland Ltd are committed to promoting traditional craft and raising awareness of the quality and quantity of handmade goods being produced in Scotland. As part of this commitment an extensive programme of workshops has been established. International and local tutors teach classes in subjects such as weaving, spinning, paper making, lampwork glass bead making and jewellery making. Students from all parts of the world have enrolled in these classes. Examples of previously run classes include rug weaving with Jason Collingwood, felt making with Ewa Kuniczak, tassel making with Anna Crutchley, tapestry weaving with Joan Baxter and knitwear design with Di Gilpin. The workshops are held in a comfortable, purpose built studio adjacent to the gallery.

Wendy Inkster

I designed and made my original bear in 1997, as a gift for my sister. My concept, to recycle an entire hand knitted Fair Isle woollen jumper into a bear, brought such a positive response that it resulted in a full-time job. All the other Burra Bears I have sewn since then have been given the same characteristics.

The iconic Fair Isle jumper represents our traditional Shetland textile culture, and is revered for it's intricate construction, but it is often thrown away when elbows are worn through, and cuffs fray.

My recycled bears are pleasant reminders of the true sensory and aesthetic values of well-made and treasured fabrics. I hope that each Burra Bear will contribute to a cleaner environment and inspire the new owner, to think about it's origins, the message it embodies, and to consider re-using other materials creatively.

Colin Smith

I work with natural fieldstone and metal. My creations reflect my enjoyment of Scottish wildlife, particularly birds.

The sculptures, range in size from large impressions of herons, eagles and hawks to smaller works depicting ducks, grouse, gulls, and even the quirky roadrunner. The sculptures have been used as focal points in garden schemes or in the home, adorning a conservatory or lounge.

Touched by Scotland

A selection of other galleries

SOUTH WEST

Crafts Gallery Griffin's Yard

North Road
South Molton
Devon EX 36 3AZ
T: 01769 574284
E: jenny@craftsgallerygriffinsyard.co.uk
www.craftsgallerygriffinsyard.co.uk
Open: Monday-Saturday 10am-5pm

Lantic Gallery

38 Gold Street
Tiverton
Devon
EX16 8PY
T: 01884 259888
E: info@lanticgallery.co.uk
www.lanticgallery.co.uk
Open: Monday-Friday 10am-5pm,
Saturday-10am-4pm

Ann Powell – *butterfly necklace with tourmalines,* her work can be seen at South West galleries – 6, 26 & 46

WESSEX

Bettles Gallery

82 Christchurch Road
Ringwood
Hampshire BH24 1DR
T: 01425 470410
www.bettles.net
Open: Wednesday-Saturday 10am-5pm or
by appointment

Bristol Guild of Applied Art

68-70 Park Street
Bristol
BS1 5JY
T: 01179 265548
E: info@bristolguild.co.uk
www.bristolguild.co.uk
Open: Monday-Saturday 10am-5pm

Gallery on the Bridge

The Street
Castle Combe
Wiltshire
SN14 7HU
T: 01249 782201
www.galleryonthebridge.co.uk
Open: Summer – every day 9.30am-5.30pm
Winter – everyday 10am-4.30pm
Closed Christmas Day

A selection of other galleries

WESSEX
Makers
6 Bath Place
Taunton
Somerset TA1 4ER
T: 01823 251121
E: info@makerstaunton.co.uk
www.makerstaunton.co.uk
Open: Monday-Saturday 9am-5pm

Diana Porter Contemporary Jewellery
33 Park Street
Bristol
BS1 5NH
T: 01179 090225
E: post@dianaporter.co.uk
www.dianaporter.co.uk
Open: Monday-Friday 100am-5.45pm

LONDON & SOUTH EAST
The Modern Artists Gallery
High Street
Whitchurch-on-Thames
Near Reading
Berkshire RG8 7EX
T: 01189 845893
E: info@modernartistsgallery.com
www.modernartistsgallery.com
Open: Wednesday-Friday 10am-5.30pm,
Saturday 10am-4pm or by appointment

EASTERN
Bury St. Edmunds Art Gallery and Craft Shop
Market Cross, Cornhill
Bury St. Edmunds
Suffolk IP33 1BT
T: 01284 762081
E: enquiries@burystedmundsartgallery.org
www.burystedmundsartgallery.org
Open: Tuesday-Saturday 10.30am-5pm

Harding House Gallery
Steep Hill
Lincoln
LN2 1LT
T: 01522 523537
E: info@hardinghousegallery.co.uk
www.hardinghousegallery.co.uk
Open: Daily 10am-5pm

CENTRAL
The City Gallery
90 Granby Street
Leicester
LE1 1DJ
T: 01162 252060
E: city.gallery@leicester.gov.uk
www.leicester.gov.uk/citygallery
Open: Tuesday-Friday 11am-6pm,
Saturday 10a.m-5pm

A selection of other galleries

CENTRAL

Warwick Gallery
14 Smith Street
Warwick CV34 4HH
T: 01926 495880
E: see website
www.art-is-a-tart.com
Open: Monday-Saturday 9.30am-5.30pm
Open some Sundays please
telephone to check

Warwick Gallery
82 Regent Street
Royal Leamington Spa
CV32 4NS
T: 01926 422833
www.art-is-a-tart.com
Open: Monday-Saturday 9.30am-5.30pm
Open some Sundays please
telephone to check

NORTHERN

The ArtRoom Gallery
4, Oak Grove
Bridge Street
Garstang
Lancashire PR3 1LE
T: 01995 600400
E: helen@artroomgallery.co.uk
www.artroomgallery.co.uk
Open: Tuesday-Saturday 10am-5pm

NORTHERN

Booth House Gallery/Jim Robison Ceramics
3 Booth House Lane
Holmfirth
Huddersfield
HD9 2QT
T: 01484 685270
E: jim.robison@virgin.net
www.jimrobison.co.uk or
www.boothhousegallery.co.uk
Open: Saturday /Sunday noon-4pm
Mid-week times vary please telephone to check

Helen Beard – *ceramics, page 97*

SCOTLAND

The Fotheringham Gallery
78 Henderson Street
Bridge of Allan
Stirlingshire
FK9 4HS
T: 01786 832861
E: info@fotheringhamgallery.co.uk
www.fotheringhamgallery.co.uk
Open: Monday-Saturday 10a.m-5.30pm

BCF Books

www.bcfbooks.co.uk

Galleries of Australia and New Zealand

Galleries and showrooms like those listed in Galleries of Australia and New Zealand are central to the infrastructure of collectors and consumers, organisations and institutions that support contemporary designers and makers. In these galleries makers can not only exhibit and sell their own work but also most effectively see that of their contemporaries. At the same time, with all these summaries in one portable place this guide is a most useful directory for buyers. While it will be of

special benefit to travellers wanting to plan an itinerary around the kinds of objects in which they are interested, this round-up, reaching widely across both countries, is also of value to locals who want a ready reference to outlets close to them.

It is much more than a collecting and shopping guide. A number of these galleries were established decades ago. Over the years, and up to the present, others have emerged to join them, demonstrating a continuing interest in supporting both makers and their audiences. Brought together, the individual stories of history and purpose provide an introduction to the broader context of crafts and design in Australia and New Zealand.

A section from the Foreword for Galleries of Australia and New Zealand, written by Grace Cochrane who is an independent writer and curator, and former senior curator of the Powerhouse Museum, Sydney, Australia.

Illustration: The Hive, ACT Australia

The first edition of
Galleries of Australia and New Zealand
ISBN: 9780955002656   **RRP** is £10.50 + PP£1.50
Special Offer for readers of the Craft Galleries Guide
£9 incl P & P Please send cheques,
made payable to BCF Books, to :

Burton Cottage Farm, East Coker,
Yeovil, Somerset BA22 9LS
T: 01935 862731
E: cm@craftgalleries.co.uk
www.bcfbooks.co.uk

CRAFTS

THE MAGAZINE FOR CONTEMPORARY CRAFT

SUBSCRIBE TODAY AND RECEIVE YOUR FIRST ISSUE FREE

Crafts magazine is the UK'S leading authority on decorative and applied arts. Published every two months by the Crafts Council, *Crafts* supplies in-depth coverage and debate across the full spectrum of crafts disciplines, showcasing the best work in ceramics, textiles, jewellery, wood, furniture, glass, fashion and architecture. If you're looking for inspiration and vital information, *Crafts* is the only resource you need.

Subscribe to *Crafts* magazine today and receive 1 issue absolutely free – that's 7 issues for the price of 6.
A one year subscription costs £32.

To take advantage of this special offer, simply quote 'CGG 2007' when you order.
Subscribe online now by visiting our website
www.craftscouncil.org.uk/crafts
or choose one of the following methods:
T +44 (0) 207 806 2542
F +44 (0) 207 837 0858
E subscriptions@craftscouncil.org.uk
or write to us at:
Subscriptions Department
Crafts magazine
44a Pentonville Road, London N1 9BY, United Kingdom

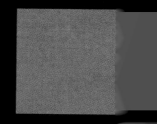

CRAFTWORKER'S YEAR BOOK

DIARY OF BRITISH EVENTS – OVER 1,500 CRAFT FAIRS & EXHIBITIONS, CRAFT MARQUEES AT MAJOR SHOWS, CRAFT MARKETS, SHOWCASES, FESTIVALS – ALL LISTED WITH DATE, VENUE & NAME OF ORGANISER

ORGANISERS IN DETAIL: WHO, WHERE, WHAT THEY CHARGE, WEBSITES, BOOKING PROFILE, SELECTION POLICY AND WHICH MONTHS THEIR FAIRS TAKE PLACE.

DIRECTORY OF SUPPLIERS OVER 200 SUPPLIERS OF CRAFT & ART MATERIALS AND EQUIPMENT

COURSE CO-ORDINATORS: A ROUND-UP OF OVER 80 CRAFT SKILLS COURSE PROVIDERS ...OUR BIGGEST EVER LIST!

DIRECTORY OF GUILDS, ASSOCIATIONS & SOCIETIES AND ADVISORY/SUPPORT BODIES - OVER 200 LISTINGS

PUBLICATIONS GUIDE – DETAILS ON SPECIALIST TITLES PLUS SUBSCRIPTION PRICES AND SPECIAL OFFERS AROUND 60 MAGAZINES LISTED

STILL ONLY
£21.95
INC. POSTAGE

By Mail: Write Angle Press, 16 Holm Oak Drive, Madeley, Crewe CW3 9HR
CHEQUES PAYABLE TO: WRITE ANGLE PRESS
CARD PAYMENTS: **01782 750986**

Arts Council England's Own Art scheme is designed to make it easy and affordable for everyone to buy original, high quality contemporary art and craft.

You can borrow up to £2,000, or as little as £100, to be paid back in equal instalments over a period of 10 months – completely interest free.

Own Art is available through selected galleries across England and Scotland that specialise in the sale of contemporary arts and crafts. Customers can choose to buy or commission work in any media from jewellery and ceramics to hand crafted furniture and textiles. A full list of participating outlets can be found on the Own Art website **www.ownart.org.uk**

To apply for membership of the Own Art scheme please visit our website or telephone Arts Council England on 0845 300 6200 and ask for an application pack.

Typical 0% APR

Arts Council England is the national development agency for the arts. We want the arts to be at the heart of our national life. Providing interest free loans is one of the ways we encourage people throughout England to experience and enjoy art of the highest quality.

Own Art is operated by ArtCo Trading Ltd, a wholly owned subsidiary of Arts Council England. Registered Address: Arts Council England, North East, Central Square, Forth Street, Newcastle upon Tyne, NE1 3PJ.

Craft Galleries Insurance

For full details contact:

T.H. March & Co Limited
Hare Park House
Yelverton Business Park
Yelverton
PL20 7LS

Tel: 01822 855555
Fax: 01822 855566
E-mail: insurance@thmarch.co.uk
website: wwwthmarch.co.uk

TH March is a trading style of
TH March & Co Limited
TH March & Co Limited is authorised and
regulated by the Financial Services Authority

Picture courtesy of the Devon Guild of Craftsmen
E-mail: devonguild@crafts.org.uk
 website: www.crafts.corg.uk

Galleries Index

A=Automata, **Ac**=Acrylic, **B**=Baskets, **Bk**=Bookbinding, **Cal**=Calligraphy, **C**=Ceramics, **Cl**=Collage, **DD**=Decoy Ducks, **E**=Enamel, **E/P/W**=Etchings, Prints & Woodcuts, **F**=Furniture, **G**=Glass, **J**=Jewellery, **L**=Leather, **Li**=Lighting, **M**=Metalwork, **Min**=Miniatures, **Mx**=Mixed media, **P**= paperwork, **PM**=Papiér Mâché, **Ph**=Photographs, **SC**=Sculptural Ceramics, **S**=Sculpture, **Sl**=Silver, **St**= Stone, **T**=Toys, **Tx**=Textiles, **W**=Wood.
The majority of galleries also sell original paintings and many sell cards.

Key: Map reference number – Gallery – Media stocked – Page number

Key: Map reference number – Gallery – **Media stocked** – Page number

Key: Map reference number – Gallery – **Media stocked** – Page number

Makers Index

Index Key The gallery index numbers (they are **NOT page numbers**) listed after media, relate to the other galleries, participating in this book, with whom that maker exhibits. The blue page number indicates the makers' main entry or photograph. A second page number (prefixed with P) indicates that the maker has an extra photograph on that page.

*Key: Maker's name, medium, **index numbers of other Galleries where work can be seen** - Page number/s*

Key: Maker's name, *medium*, **index numbers of other Galleries where work can be seen** – *Page number/s*   347

Key: Maker's name, *medium*, **index numbers of other Galleries where work can be seen** – *Page number/s*

Key: Maker's name, *medium*, **index numbers of other Galleries where work can be seen** – *Page number/s*   349

    Key: Maker's name, *medium,* **index numbers of other Galleries where work can be seen** – *Page number/s*

M

Key: Maker's name, *medium*, **index numbers of other Galleries where work can be seen** – Page number/s 351

*Key: Maker's name, medium, **index numbers of other Galleries where work can be seen** – Page number/s*

Key: Maker's name, *medium*, **index numbers of other Galleries where work can be seen** – *Page number/s*   353

*Key: Maker's name, medium, **index numbers of other Galleries where work can be seen** – Page number/s*

Abbott & Ellwood page 325

Although every effort has been made to ensure that the information given in this book is correct at the time of publication, the publishers cannot accept responsibility for any errors.